The Telegraph

BIG BOOK OF QUICK CROSSWORDS

7

The Telegraph

BIG BOOK OF QUICK CROSSWORDS 7

hamlyn

An Hachette UK Company
www.hachette.co.uk

First published in Great Britain in 2020 by
Hamlyn, an imprint of Octopus Publishing Group Ltd,
Carmelite House, 50 Victoria Embankment, London EC4Y 0DZ
www.octopusbooks.co.uk

ISBN 978-0-600-63689-2

A CIP catalogue record for this book is available from the British Library.

Printed and bound in the UK

10 9 8 7 6 5 4 3 2 1

This material was previously published in *Telegraph All New Quick 8*, *Telegraph All New Quick 9*, *Telegraph All New Quick 10* and *Telegraph All New Quick 11*.

Telegraph Puzzles Editor: Chris Lancaster
Publishing Director: Trevor Davies
Creative Director: Jonathan Christie
Managing Editor: Sybella Stephens
Editor: Lesley Malkin
Editorial Assistant: Sarah Kyle
Page make-up: Dorchester Typesetting Group Ltd
Senior Production Manager: Peter Hunt
Production Controller: Serena Savini

PUZZLES

1

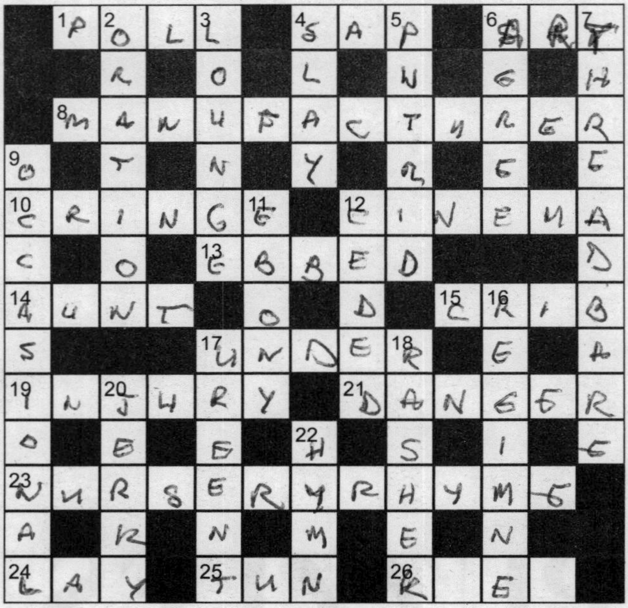

Across

1 *Vote* (4)
4 *Weaken; tree fluid* (3)
6 *Skill, craft* (3)
8 Industrialist (12)
10 Flinch (6)
12 Picture house (6)
13 Receded (5)
14 Female relative (4)
15 Baby's bed (4)
17 Beneath (5)
19 Hurt (6)
21 Peril (6)
23 Children's verse (7,5)
24 Non-clerical, amateur (3)
25 Cask (3)
26 Row; foul (4)

Down

2 Speech (7)
3 Living room (6)
4 Kill (4)
5 Rotten (6)
6 Concur (5)
7 Worn out (10)
9 Intermittent; now and then (10)
11 Hard, black wood (5)
12 Yielded (5)
16 Diet (7)
17 Pressing, important (6)
18 Bacon slice (6)
20 Spasmodic (5)
22 Song of praise (4)

2

Across

1 *Box; pole* (4)
5 *Cathedral town* (4)
7 Impressive (7)
8 Glue (8)
10 Wicked (4)
12 Russian emperor (4)
14 Balderdash (8)
16 Unworried (8)
17 12 months (4)
18 Hero (4)
19 Permit (8)
22 Goddess of retribution (7)
23 Expectant, eager (4)
24 Otherwise (4)

Down

1 Couch (4)
2 Run; nation (4)
3 Novice (8)
4 Mislay (4)
5 Graveyard (8)
6 Bawl, yowl (4)
9 Reject (7)
11 Immediate (7)
13 German white wine (8)
15 Unnecessary (8)
18 Thought (4)
19 Grave (4)
20 Trick (4)
21 Brink (4)

The Telegraph

3

Across

1 *Daze* (6)
5 *Afterwards* (5)
9 Dishonest (9)
10 Sir — Rice, lyricist (3)
11 Metallic element (3)
12 Trojan War leader (9)
14 Outfit; fix (3)
16 Savoury jelly (5)
18 Knight's title (3)
19 Increase in loudness (9)
21 Wager (3)
22 Afternoon meal (3)
23 Long-snouted animal (9)
25 Weighty (5)
26 River Wear city (6)

Down

2 French sculptor (5)
3 Kurt Cobain group (7)
4 Historical period (3)
5 Gatehouse (5)
6 Lockjaw (7)
7 Payment (12)
8 Brittle sweet (12)
13 Poplar tree (5)
15 Caribbean country (7)
17 Rich soup (7)
20 Cautious (5)
21 Corkwood (5)
24 Extremely foolish (3)

The Telegraph

4

Across

1 *Inventor* (4)
5 *Comfort* (4)
7 Egg white (7)
8 Anti-Communist US senator (8)
10 Couple (4)
12 Golf club (4)
14 Promptly! (4-4)
16 Appraisal (8)
17 Old Testament prophet (4)
18 Pierce (4)
19 English novelist (8)
22 Break up (7)
23 Insignificant (4)
24 Course of exercises and postures (4)

Down

1 Ointment (4)
2 Molten rock (4)
3 Impediment (8)
4 TV award (4)
5 Surround (8)
6 Dutch cheese (4)
9 Outdoor game (7)
11 Self-aggrandising conduct (3-4)
13 Drudge (8)
15 Not compulsory (8)
18 Filter, riddle (4)
19 Job (4)
20 Woman (4)
21 Mediterranean island (4)

The Telegraph

5

Across

1 *Fuzz* (4)
4 *Exploit* (4)
8 *Stun* (4)
9 Paterfamilias (9)
11 Small hole (6)
13 Accused (7)
15 African (6)
16 Chauffeur (6)
18 Stimulate (6)
20 Poetic unit (6)
22 Balm (7)
23 Type of script (6)
25 Passable (9)
26 Urge (4)
27 Edge of pavement (4)
28 Oil reservoir (4)

Down

2 Regrettably (4)
3 Seldom (6)
4 Muffle impact (6)
5 Go beyond (6)
6 Gad about (9)
7 Loaned (4)
10 Moisturise (7)
12 Auks (anag.) (4)
13 Irritation (9)
14 Legal case (7)
17 Wander (4)
19 Encipher (6)
20 Brilliant (6)
21 Records (6)
23 Part of eye (4)
24 Svelte (4)

6

Across

1 *Agents* (5)
4 *Twists* (5)
10 Tag line (anag.); glue (7)
11 Sound broadcast (5)
12 Taunt (5)
13 Thrown out (7)
15 Big hair? (4)
17 African tongue (5)
19 Go round (5)
22 Alone (4)
25 Took over (7)
27 Butch (5)
29 Imprecations (5)
30 Promote (7)
31 Played (5)
32 Rude gesture (1-4)

Down

2 Dotty dance? (5)
3 Beseech (7)
5 Custom (5)
6 Party girl? (7)
7 Form of quartz (5)
8 Wrath (5)
9 Verbose (5)
14 Fleshy cheek (4)
16 Coalesce (4)
18 Living in water (7)
20 Pays deference to (7)
21 Rubenesque (5)
23 Abhorrence (5)
24 Naps (5)
26 Glue (5)
28 Metallic noise (5)

7

Across

1 *Blood* (4)
4 *Past* (4)
8 *19th-century French novelist* (4)
9 Soft Normandy cheese (9)
11 Small purple plum (6)
13 Round (7)
15 Dawdle (6)
16 Odeon perhaps (6)
18 Witty answer (6)
20 Overcharge (6)
22 Innocent-looking (3-4)
23 Aromatic plant (6)
25 Indian killers of snakes and rats (9)
26 Den (4)
27 Swelling by eye (4)
28 Jug (4)

Down

2 All right (4)
3 Grant immunity (6)
4 Babble (6)
5 Scandinavian (6)
6 Supported (9)
7 Thread (4)
10 Without a word (7)
12 Pole (4)
13 Numerical fact (9)
14 Succession (7)
17 Tip (4)
19 Complete construction of a building (3,3)
20 Manchester United manager familiarly (6)
21 A. A. Milne's eternal pessimist (3-3)
23 Grasp (4)
24 To celebrate; village fair (4)

8

Across

1 *Respect* (6)
4 *Nobody* (4)
8 Cheerful (6)
9 Previously (6)
10 Vary (5)
11 Fortress (7)
13 Self-satisfied (4)
15 Label (3)
16 Overcast (4)
18 Nobleness (7)
20 Boisterous (5)
23 Consequence (6)
24 Kidnap (6)
25 Annoy (4)
26 Corkscrew (6)

Down

1 Gangster (7)
2 Innocent (5)
3 Unattractive (4)
5 Casual (7)
6 Spooky (5)
7 Condense (7)
12 Law (7)
14 Respectable (7)
17 Militant (7)
19 Deduce (5)
21 Command (5)
22 Moist (4)

9

Across

1 *Snooker rod* (3)
3 *Amuse* (6)
7 American state (7)
8 & 14 Down Melted cheese on toast (5,7)
10 Skilful (4)
11 South African mammals (8)
13 Sailing ship (6)
15 Game's participant (6)
17 Word-writer for songs (8)
18 Office note (4)
21 Jewish teacher (5)
22 Pasta dish (7)
23 Mean (6)
24 Arid (3)

Down

1 Principal (5)
2 Asteroid (4)
3 Locomotion (6)
4 Yellow (8)
5 Go-to-sleep song (7)
6 Of the lower jaw (10)
9 Melodramatic (10)
12 Meeting point (8)
14 *See 8 Across*
16 Fish-eating bird (6)
19 Resin (5)
20 Roman poet (4)

The Telegraph

10

Across

1 *Male lover* (4)
4 *Slightly burnt* (7)
8 Pertaining to marriage (8)
9 Short sleep (3)
11 Nauseous (6)
13 Boer statesman (6)
14 Metric weight unit (5)
15 Lopsided (4)
17 Consider (4)
18 Material (5)
20 Fix on (6)
21 Football team? (6)
24 Diamonds (slang) (3)
25 Silent monk (8)
26 Furthest point (7)
27 Royal house (4)

Down

2 Arouse (5)
3 Not fair (6)
4 Barred container (4)
5 Entice (6)
6 Default (7)
7 Behaviour (10)
10 Greenish blue (10)
12 Youngster (5)
13 Table implement (5)
16 Hideaway (7)
18 Grass-cutter (6)
19 Not rigid (6)
22 Face-protector (5)
23 Mist (4)

The Telegraph

11

Across

1 *Russian city* (6)
4 *German city* (6)
9 *Indian or Thai?* (5)
10 Reading desk (7)
11 Snake-like fish (3)
12 Pondered (5)
13 Mythical creature (7)
15 Aristocratic lady (11)
19 Cause of trouble (7)
20 Burst of light (5)
21 Anger (3)
22 Infection from wound (7)
24 Prejudiced person (5)
25 Suitable to farm (6)
26 Lack of interest (6)

Down

1 Unpleasant air (6)
2 In good order (9)
3 Possessed (5)
5 Ritual anointing (7)
6 Cold demeanour (3)
7 Making sharp (6)
8 Stage magician (11)
14 Heavy attack (9)
16 Army officer (7)
17 Aunt of Wooster (6)
18 Church room (6)
20 Jazz style (5)
23 Hot drink (3)

The Telegraph

12

Across

1 *Hotel* (3)
3 *Chester's river* (3)
5 *Hang* (4)
7 *Impenetrable* (5)
8 Born yesterday (3-3)
10 Ape (4)
11 Emblems of rank (8)
13 Gaga (6)
14 Patterned material (6)
17 Holiday (8)
19 German woman (4)
21 Seem (6)
22 Android (5)
23 Covet (4)
24 Gammon (3)
25 Bid (3)

Down

1 Vacillating (10)
2 Skittle (7)
3 Slimming plan (4)
4 Stopping (6)
5 Bodily (8)
6 Stocking material (5)
9 Insolvency (10)
12 Left tray (anag.) (8)
15 Rope-dancer (7)
16 Quarter (6)
18 Male fowl (5)
20 Topmost edge (4)

13

Across

1 *Knight's title* (3)
3 *Equipment* (3)
5 *Fed up* (5)
8 Open sore (5)
9 Capital of China (7)
10 Unable to hear (4)
11 Resort in Cornwall (8)
13 — Bible (6)
14 A Bordeaux wine (6)
17 Gather (8)
19 Burden (4)
22 Outfit (7)
23 Regal (5)
24 Enjoyed (5)
25 Gender (3)
26 Female sheep (3)

Down

1 Crew (5)
2 — the Lionheart (7)
3 Church (4)
4 Pill (6)
5 Snowstorm (8)
6 Rule (5)
7 Be sidetracked (7)
12 Absinthe (8)
13 Steady (7)
15 Pointed beard (7)
16 Scottish castle (6)
18 Cane; criticism (5)
20 Work out (5)
21 Nub (4)

14

Across

1 *Ship's company* (4)
4 *Greek prophetess* (5)
8 Correct (8)
9 Guide; metallic element (4)
10 Prosecuted (4)
11 Occurred (8)
12 Coma, lethargy (6)
14 Sorry (6)
16 Mishap (8)
19 Too (4)
20 Diplomacy (4)
21 Desperado (8)
22 Mistake (5)
23 Biblical garden (4)

Down

2 Circular (5)
3 Climate (7)
4 Slumber (5)
5 Understand (7)
6 Depart (5)
7 Exonerate (6)
13 Artist (7)
14 Train, escort (7)
15 Province of Ireland; overcoat (6)
17 Pursue (5)
18 Zealous (5)
19 Passage (5)

The Telegraph

15

Across

1 *Small restaurant* (5)
4 *Tender* (4)
7 Leave out (4)
8 Forceful (8)
9 Meet (9)
10 Mole (3)
12 Predicament (6)
14 Burroughs hero (6)
16 Be in debt (3)
18 Peevish (9)
21 Avoid (8)
22 Leaf of metal (4)
23 Agitate (4)
24 Recess in wall (5)

Down

1 Like a devil (7)
2 Speculative (8)
3 Bird (5)
4 Japanese wrestling (4)
5 Approach (3-2)
6 Indication of danger (6)
11 Fertile (8)
13 Fairness (6)
15 Insulting (7)
17 Joint (5)
19 Mature (5)
20 Deride (4)

The Telegraph

16

Across

1 *Solid fuel* (4)
3 *Led (meeting)* (7)
8 Office (6)
9 Irritable (6)
10 Pull apart (8)
11 Wanes (4)
12 Climb (6)
15 Devious (6)
17 Grow weary (4)
19 Drool (8)
22 Leg bone (6)
23 Intrepid (6)
24 Quarantine (7)
25 Intend (4)

Down

1 Oil; rough (5)
2 Ordinary (7)
4 Milliners (7)
5 Become hardened (5)
6 Show (7)
7 Cougar (4)
13 Ripostes (7)
14 Aloof (7)
16 Opposite (7)
18 Thin soup (5)
20 Boys (4)
21 Saw; joint (5)

17

Across

1 *Former Indian coins* (5)
4 *Hardwood tree* (4)
8 *Away* (3)
9 Hearth (9)
10 Crafty (4)
11 Reprove (8)
12 Employ (3)
13 Warbles (6)
14 Dummies (6)
16 Offer (3)
17 Innkeeper (8)
18 Smudge (4)
20 Go-betweens (9)
21 Broadcast (3)
22 Avid (4)
23 Leg joint (5)

Down

1 Distantly (7)
2 Nowhere to live (2,5,5)
3 Secure (4)
4 Outburst (6)
5 Authorised (8)
6 Public land (8,4)
7 Grid, netting (4)
11 Fool (3)
12 Last (8)
14 Flipper (3)
15 Release (3,4)
16 Large primate (6)
17 Great ceremony (4)
19 Continent (4)

18

Across

1 *Reproductions* (6)
5 *Sear* (4)
8 *Chinese porcelain* (4)
9 Gatecrasher (8)
10 Turn upside down (6)
11 Damage (6)
12 Social gathering (3-8)
15 Dexterous (6)
17 Tinker (6)
19 Brush cutter (8)
20 Carry (4)
21 Clarified butter (4)
22 Regard (6)

Down

2 Rule (5)
3 Disregard (7)
4 Hard-up (5)
5 Nitwit (5)
6 Artist's studio (7)
7 Dress (6)
12 Split the bill (2,5)
13 Punctual (2,4)
14 Environment (7)
16 Suppose (5)
17 Funeral song (5)
18 Supple (5)

The Telegraph

19

Across

1 *Shack* (3)
3 *Rapidity* (5)
6 *Transgress* (3)
8 *Humorous* (5)
9 Inhibit (7)
10 Copies (10)
12 Hound (3)
15 Trade (4)
17 Enfold (4)
18 Ingest (3)
22 Owner (10)
25 Disinfect (7)
26 Inappropriate (5)
27 Speck (3)
28 Steed (5)
29 Youth (3)

Down

1 Brawniest (8)
2 Palpable (8)
3 Prime (6)
4 Squalid (6)
5 Dilate (6)
6 Paradise (4)
7 Danger (4)
11 Scatter (3)
13 Appreciative (8)
14 Vivacious (8)
16 Circuit (3)
19 Channel (6)
20 Seem (6)
21 Tiny (6)
23 Bitter (4)
24 Crooked (4)

Across

1 *Brute* (5)
4 *Animal group* (4)
8 Gift from will (7)
9 Affair (5)
10 Camel-like animal (5)
11 Meet the requirements of (7)
13 Disappear (6)
15 Frank (6)
17 Similarity (7)
20 Medical cloth (5)
22 'Filthy' money (5)
23 E.g. kitchen surface (7)
24 Exam success (4)
25 Eliot's 'cruellest month' (5)

Down

1 Place of cacophony (5)
2 Person known slightly (12)
3 Classic horse race (3,4)
4 Detests (5)
5 Cook in oven (5)
6 Insurance assessor (4,8)
7 Worn at the edges (6)
12 Curve (3)
13 Feasible (6)
14 Pig (3)
16 North African country (7)
18 Musical drama (5)
19 Gapes (5)
21 Throw out (5)

The Telegraph

21

Across

1 *French capital* (5)
4 *Conclusion* (6)
9 Fabric (7)
10 Discernment (5)
11 Wild goat (4)
12 Cumulative prize (7)
13 Animal collection (3)
14 Item of footwear (4)
16 Carbonated drink (4)
18 Very small (3)
20 Siren (7)
21 Appendage; follow (4)
24 Search (5)
25 Cheer in distress (7)
26 Attempts (6)
27 Holiness (5)

Down

1 Language of group (6)
2 Firearm (5)
3 Staunch (4)
5 Wallet (8)
6 Lacking 10 (7)
7 Segregated area (6)
8 Stringed instrument (5)
13 Fanatacism (8)
15 Equine gear (7)
17 Film on tooth (6)
18 Lifting device (5)
19 Dozy (6)
22 Overhead (5)
23 Bargain (4)

22

Across

1 *Exclusive group* (6)
4 *Lofty room* (5)
8 *Be compatible* (5)
9 Baking dish (7)
10 Police search (7)
11 Break suddenly (4)
12 Following trends (3)
14 Knock down (4)
15 Disapproving sound (4)
18 Edible tuber (3)
21 Baby's biscuit (4)
23 Fine spray (7)
25 Holiday business (7)
26 Sharp weapon (5)
27 Sugary sweet (5)
28 Church official (6)

Down

1 Chirpy insect (6)
2 Mimic (7)
3 Lacking sympathy (8)
4 Large host (4)
5 Money substitute (5)
6 Light refreshment (6)
7 Thick soup (5)
13 Sanctimonious hypocrite (8)
16 Imagine guilt (7)
17 Newspaper reviewer (6)
19 Molten rock (5)
20 Old coin (6)
22 Reject contemptuously (5)
24 Cunning (4)

23

Across

1 *Punitive* (5)
5 *Act as waiter* (5)
8 *Musical exercise* (5)
9 Twist (5)
10 Went wrong (9)
11 Five-centime piece (3)
12 Foreordained (11)
15 Cactus fruit (7,4)
19 Everybody (3)
20 Patent (9)
22 Bullion bar (5)
23 Pinafore (5)
24 Native American symbol (5)
25 Pierced (by a horn) (5)

Down

1 Moneylender's premises (8)
2 A lupin (anag.) (4,2)
3 Spinning ball (3,5)
4 Strength (6)
5 Ego (4)
6 Short cut (3,3)
7 Ogled (4)
13 Handling (8)
14 Let down (8)
16 Tax, duty (6)
17 Grouty (anag.) (6)
18 Park officer (6)
20 Young horse (4)
21 Twenty quires (4)

Across

1 *Minestrone?* (4)
3 *Authorised* (8)
9 Cancel (5)
10 Chorus (7)
11 Pasty (3)
13 Snow slide (9)
14 Motive (6)
16 First child of Jacob (6)
18 Reproduce (9)
20 Female sheep (3)
22 Speech (7)
23 Slumber (5)
25 Perpetuity (8)
26 Whirlpool (4)

Down

1 Acute; pointed (5)
2 Vase (3)
4 Ceremonial; ordered (6)
5 Incite (7)
6 Cantankerous (9)
7 Portable lamp (7)
8 Request (4)
12 Ornate (9)
14 Rebuke (7)
15 Applause (7)
17 Gemstone (6)
19 Simple (4)
21 Vacant (5)
24 Finish (3)

25

Across

1 *Resentment* (5)
3 *Type of beef soup* (6)
7 Lovely (9)
9 Action; document (4)
10 Cultivate (4)
11 Swoon; indistinct (5)
13 Necessitate (6)
14 Tail off; a spill (5)
15 Cast feathers (5)
17 Still (6)
20 Foul; filthy (5)
21 Want (4)
23 Soon (4)
24 Bad dream (9)
25 Glut; surplus (6)
26 Keen (5)

Down

1 Promise (6)
2 Second-hand (4)
3 The East (6)
4 Tight (4)
5 Large spoon (5)
6 Wall painting (5)
7 German composer (9)
8 Roué (9)
11 Meadow (5)
12 Flavoursome (5)
16 Women's garments (6)
17 Postage paid label (5)
18 Agree (6)
19 Male relation (5)
22 Dreadful; grim (4)
23 Operatic song (4)

26

Across

1 *Member of the clergy* (6)
4 *Consider carefully* (5)
8 Overhead (5)
9 Answered (7)
10 Ignorant (7)
11 Monster (4)
12 Lower (3)
14 Clarified butter (4)
15 Edible grass seeds (4)
18 Observe (3)
21 Every one (4)
23 Trucks (7)
25 Ooh, spam! (anag.) (7)
26 Thick (5)
27 Female (5)
28 Gathered (6)

Down

1 Deadly epidemic (6)
2 Bear (7)
3 Works (8)
4 Cried (4)
5 Cake topping (5)
6 Concealed (6)
7 Pressed (5)
13 Jail sentence (8)
16 More flimsy (7)
17 Playground device (6)
19 Jostle (5)
20 Feature (6)
22 Maintain (5)
24 Uncovered (4)

The Telegraph

27

Across

1 *Ticket price* (4)
4 *Passageway* (5)
8 Monkey business (8)
9 Uncommon (4)
10 Touched (4)
11 Unfailing (8)
12 Mark of disgrace (6)
14 Hate (6)
16 Wild (8)
19 Fortune (4)
20 Just; market (4)
21 Scottish city (8)
22 Flower (5)
23 Appear (4)

Down

2 Berkshire racecourse (5)
3 Red Sea country (7)
4 Horrific (5)
5 Retainer (7)
6 Sign on (5)
7 Absorb (6)
13 Army officer (7)
14 Noblewoman (7)
15 Football (6)
17 Respond (5)
18 Vagrant (5)
19 Gatehouse (5)

28

Across

1 *Klondike area* (5)
4 *Match* (4)
8 Threatens (7)
9 Implied (5)
10 Relation (5)
11 On the way (2,5)
13 Swallow (6)
15 Schoolkids (6)
17 Bent (7)
20 Erect (3,2)
22 Encounters (5)
23 Everlasting (7)
24 Stallion (4)
25 Destitute (5)

Down

1 Red Sea country (5)
2 Infant school (12)
3 Part of atom (7)
4 Discernment (5)
5 Bury (5)
6 Familiar person (12)
7 Tension (6)
12 Doze (3)
13 Revenue (6)
14 Exploit (3)
16 Lots of (7)
18 Distressed (5)
19 Part of tyre (5)
21 Friendly (5)

29

Across

1 *Berthed* (6)
4 *Funeral car* (6)
7 *Savers* (8)
9 Fought against (7)
12 Engine (5)
13 Scour (5)
15 Put out (flames) (5)
16 Baghdadi, perhaps (5)
17 Manoeuvre (5)
19 Demise (5)
20 Jewish tongue (7)
24 Conrad Hilton, e.g. (8)
25 Sadness (6)
26 Tenner (anag.); cheese ingredient (6)

Down

1 Dry out (10)
2 Maritime service (10)
3 Supports (8)
4 Hinged fastener for door or lid (4)
5 Additionally (4)
6 Rescue (4)
8 Bellow (4)
10 Break-up (10)
11 Remove as heir (10)
14 Sort of view (5-3)
18 Repeat (4)
21 Keen on (4)
22 Expensive (4)
23 Demonstrate (4)

The Telegraph

30

Across

1 *Atoll* (4)
4 *Ale* (4)
8 *Woof* (4)
9 Coverlet (9)
11 Bombastic (6)
13 Brochure (7)
15 Recognition (6)
16 Defuse (6)
18 Teacher (6)
20 Misgivings (6)
22 Disgust (7)
23 Box (6)
25 Authenticated (9)
26 Boring (4)
27 Begrudge (4)
28 Naked (4)

Down

2 Outhouse (4)
3 Resulted (6)
4 Deprived (6)
5 Ecstatic (6)
6 Ridiculous (9)
7 Slip (4)
10 Obedient (7)
12 Froth (4)
13 Unhurried (9)
14 Flap (7)
17 Haze (4)
19 Celebrity (6)
20 Nauseous (6)
21 Delegate (6)
23 Cipher (4)
24 Repair (4)

The Telegraph

31

Across

1 *Specialist record company* (5)
4 *The world's longest river* (4)
7 Colossal (4)
8 Disgrace (8)
9 Sly (9)
10 Plot (3)
12 Exhausts (4,2)
14 Nag (6)
16 Make a choice (3)
18 Craggy; unrefined (5-4)
21 Sweeping inferno (8)
22 Reserve (4)
23 East Anglian marshes (4)
24 Theme (5)

Down

1 Move, affect (7)
2 Lessen (8)
3 Live (5)
4 Cite (4)
5 Spear (5)
6 Stampede (6)
11 Ban (8)
13 Aversion (6)
15 Modified shotgun (4-3)
17 Balance (5)
19 Shimmer (5)
20 Starting price (4)

32

Across

7 *Further up* (6)
8 *Lines of waiters* (6)
10 Gandhi's title (7)
11 German philosopher (5)
12 Jacob's brother (4)
13 Northumbrian king (5)
17 Follow stealthily (5)
18 Persian ruler (4)
22 Nut-bearing tree (5)
23 Square number (7)
24 Edible crustacean (6)
25 Plan (6)

Down

1 Complaint (7)
2 Intellectual (7)
3 Landing stage (5)
4 Flowering shrub (7)
5 Shift (5)
6 Song of praise (5)
9 Wanton destruction (9)
14 Alexandrian astronomer (7)
15 Criminals (7)
16 TV station (7)
19 Deep gulf (5)
20 Sort of blue (5)
21 Precise (5)

33

Across

1 *Grind* (4)
3 *Journey up* (6)
9 Deep regret (7)
10 Slant of surface (5)
11 Prime number (3)
12 American state (9)
13 European river (6)
14 A confused mixture (6)
16 Cover for bed (9)
19 Snake-like fish (3)
21 Killed (5)
22 Like type of desk (4-3)
23 Automatic (6)
24 Enthusiasm (4)

Down

1 Deserve (5)
2 Personal satire (7)
4 Later on (12)
5 Roof's overhang (5)
6 One lute (anag.); a solvent (7)
7 Bit jutting out (12)
8 Eager (4)
13 Kitchen sideboard (7)
15 Respire (7)
17 Doc? Grumpy? (5)
18 Monster (4)
20 Part of jacket (5)

34

Across

1 *Ponder (over)* (4)
4 *Related* (4)
8 *Become weary* (4)
9 Catapult (9)
11 Zilch (6)
13 Wander (7)
15 Bogged down by tedium (2,1,3)
16 Feeble-minded person (6)
18 Idle chat (6)
20 Nude dash (6)
22 Small newspaper (7)
23 Election (6)
25 Mars (3,6)
26 Cudgel (4)
27 Prevent (4)
28 Stupid (4)

Down

2 Unsightly (4)
3 Loiter (6)
4 Concur (6)
5 Pressed (6)
6 Shamed (9)
7 Finest (4)
10 Canadian city (7)
12 Vocalise (4)
13 Magnificent tomb (9)
14 Accountant (7)
17 Peer (4)
19 Copyright (6)
20 Pupils (anag.) (4-2)
21 Coarse (6)
23 Rear (4)
24 Complaint (4)

The Telegraph

35

Across

1 *Christmas-time* (4)
4 *People renting* (7)
8 Curved sword (8)
9 Sense of self (3)
11 Rather obese (6)
13 Superior nun (6)
14 Bird of prey (5)
15 Mountain goat (4)
17 Famous person (4)
18 Use of language (5)
20 Priesthood (6)
21 Countryman (6)
24 Charged particle (3)
25 Rejection of religion (8)
26 Stupid fellow (7)
27 Angry outburst (4)

Down

2 Not censored (5)
3 White fur (6)
4 Unwilling (4)
5 Professional writer (6)
6 Fundamental component (7)
7 A minimum of money (10)
10 One's original idea (10)
12 Foppish fellow (5)
13 Mixture of metals (5)
16 Everlasting (7)
18 Large lizard (6)
19 Personal guide (6)
22 Worker in stone (5)
23 Sheep pen (4)

36

Across

7 *Evil, foul* (4)
8 *Hostelry* (3)
9 *Boyfriend; dandy* (4)
10 Small crustacean (6)
11 Slackness (6)
12 Untruth; recline (3)
13 Commend (6)
14 Respond (6)
16 Young swan (6)
19 Opportunity (6)
21 Court (3)
22 Mob (6)
24 Save (6)
25 Too (4)
26 Fasten (3)
27 Every (4)

Down

1 Shrivel (6)
2 Mockery (8)
3 Easy; plain (6)
4 Fisherman (6)
5 Wild goat (4)
6 Repartee (6)
15 Hand over (8)
17 Annual (6)
18 A score (6)
19 Stays (6)
20 Support (6)
23 Ink smudge (4)

37

Across

1 *Bunk; mooring* (5)
4 *Make of car* (6)
9 Diplomatic (7)
10 Precise (5)
11 Merit (4)
12 Non-believer (7)
13 Equality (3)
14 Rant; party (4)
16 Inflamed eyelid (4)
18 Healthy (3)
20 Regain (7)
21 Bucket (4)
24 Guide; bullock (5)
25 Young tree (7)
26 Cad (6)
27 Perfume (5)

Down

1 Sour; a beer (6)
2 Happen again (5)
3 Axe handle (4)
5 Purple gem (8)
6 Attribute (7)
7 Property (6)
8 Obvious (5)
13 Contrary (8)
15 Old (7)
17 Rubber (6)
18 New (5)
19 Disembark; on fire (6)
22 Supple (5)
23 Musical work (4)

38

Across

1 *Gaze* (5)
4 *Orson —, actor* (6)
7 Word-for-word (7)
8 Setback (4)
10 Male duck (5)
11 Polishing cloth (7)
14 Underworld river (4)
16 Revolve (6)
18 Collision (6)
21 Singing voice (4)
23 Russian revolutionary (7)
26 Heavenly being (5)
27 Factory (4)
28 African country (7)
29 Tell (6)
30 Jus (5)

Down

1 Unity (10)
2 Lure (7)
3 Intensely serious (7)
4 With enthusiasm (6)
5 Zodiac sign (5)
6 Significant period (5)
9 Butterfly (10)
12 Way out (4)
13 Peak; beat (3)
15 Hard wood (4)
17 Behind (3)
19 Grumbling (7)
20 African republic (7)
22 College (6)
24 Edible bulb (5)
25 Burst of firing (5)

39

Across

1 *Clawed foot* (3)
3 *Masticate* (4)
5 *Dupe* (4)
8 Deceptive appearance (8)
10 Daze (4)
11 Rubbish (3)
13 Shelf (5)
14 Shoulder insignia (9)
16 Scottish town (3)
17 In addition (3)
19 Careless (9)
21 Abraham's son (5)
22 Black (3)
24 Other (4)
25 Pickle (8)
26 Window frame (4)
27 Sort (4)
28 Inquire (3)

Down

1 Couple (4)
2 Droop (4)
3 Moroccan city (10)
4 Missile (6)
6 Current (2-2-4)
7 Arthurian knight (8)
9 Slightly crazy (5)
12 Referendum (10)
14 Lack of difficulty (8)
15 US state (8)
18 Start (5)
20 Fine assemblage (6)
22 Indonesian island (4)
23 Hard wood (4)

40

Across

1 *Challenge* (4)
4 *Submerged rocks* (4)
8 *Weapons* (4)
9 Buyer (9)
11 Agreed (6)
13 Weakness (7)
15 E.g. ladybird (6)
16 Cup holder (6)
18 Headings (6)
20 Run naked (6)
22 Peeved (7)
23 Promenade (6)
25 Recent past (9)
26 Shade (4)
27 Catch sight of (4)
28 Squad (4)

Down

2 Adjoin (4)
3 Accompany (6)
4 Band's assistant (6)
5 Occurrences (6)
6 Forecast (9)
7 Second-hand (4)
10 Ruler's family (7)
12 Assist (crime) (4)
13 Tan figure (anag) (9)
14 So soon? (7)
17 Garden tool (4)
19 Shows scorn (6)
20 Gently (6)
21 Rue (6)
23 Compassion (4)
24 Information (4)

41

Across

1 *Female horse* (4)
4 *Understand; view* (3)
6 *Stoop* (3)
9 *Pigeon sound* (3)
10 Hebrew scholar (5)
11 Proper; sedate (5)
12 Furthest (9)
15 Soothsayer (7-6)
19 Rookie (American) (9)
21 More racy (5)
22 Fruit of oak (5)
24 Form of water (3)
25 Oui (3)
26 Mischief-maker (3)
27 Skating jump (4)

Down

2 A redtop (anag.) (7)
3 Mistake (5)
4 Weep (3)
5 Letter (7)
6 Desolate (5)
7 Savage (4)
8 Shabby (7)
13 Fat (5)
14 Tanned (7)
16 Promote (7)
17 Like a lion (7)
18 Wharves (5)
20 Japanese assassin (5)
21 Flock of birds (4)
23 Lummox (3)

42

Across

1 *Secure* (4)
4 *Fruit* (6)
7 Fuss (3)
9 Self-satisfied (4)
10 French game (8)
11 Chatter (3)
12 Dull pain (4)
13 Auditory device (8)
16 Benefactress (4,9)
19 Personality (8)
23 Hebridean island (4)
24 Finish (3)
25 Large bottle of champagne; a Rome job (anag.) (8)
26 Wading bird (4)
27 Flightless bird (3)
28 River (6)
29 Play without dialogue (4)

Down

2 Steinbeck novel (2,4,3,3)
3 Rough-edged (7)
4 Small thicket (5)
5 Record (5)
6 Stock farm (5)
8 Period of five years (12)
14 Mature (5)
15 Trophy (3)
17 Wager (3)
18 Heavy element (7)
20 Snare (5)
21 Combined (2,3)
22 ME country (5)

The Telegraph

43

Across

1 *Further* (4)
3 *Fine* (4)
9 *Concern* (5)
10 Bland (9)
11 Scrounge (5)
12 Sonority (9)
15 Reluctant (6)
17 Congenital (6)
19 Fake (9)
21 Custom (5)
23 Abstemious (9)
24 Malice (5)
25 Standard (4)
26 Shambles (4)

Down

1 Motherly (8)
2 Withstood (8)
4 Seas (6)
5 Perceive (7)
6 Manipulated (4)
7 Yield (4)
8 Diligent (4)
13 Drool (8)
14 Parsimony (8)
16 Infatuated (7)
18 Bubble (6)
20 Summit (4)
21 Myriad (4)
22 Lure (4)

The Telegraph

44

Across

1 *Farewell* (5)
4 *Go to ground* (4)
8 Attire (7)
9 Insect (5)
10 Native African (5)
11 Lockjaw (7)
13 Second World War battle (6)
15 Slightly windy (6)
17 Setting (7)
20 Social group (5)
22 Passport stamps (5)
23 Concentrated (7)
24 Legend (4)
25 Yorks city (5)

Down

1 Panic (5)
2 Splendour (12)
3 Ex-USSR country (7)
4 Pottery town (5)
5 Small hooter (5)
6 Representative example (12)
7 One of the Channel Islands (6)
12 Recede (3)
13 Recess in wall (6)
14 Blend (3)
16 Musical performance (7)
18 Dissertation (5)
19 Part of leg (5)
21 Fencing swords (5)

45

Across

1 *Saying* (5)
4 *Thousand thousand* (7)
8 Form of Buddhism (3)
9 Mountain pass (3)
10 Bottomless pit (5)
11 Scope (5)
12 Courage (7)
15 Not false (4)
17 Indifference (6)
19 Modify (6)
22 Hemispherical roof (4)
24 Overcome by force (7)
26 Meat (5)
28 Design (5)
30 Lettuce (3)
31 Cricket extra (3)
32 Kit for baby (7)
33 Leavening agent (5)

Down

1 Polish dance (7)
2 Inert gas (5)
3 'The Scottish play' (7)
4 Californian beach (6)
5 South American mammal (5)
6 Creeper (3)
7 Unpleasant (5)
13 480 or 500 sheets (4)
14 Flightless bird (3)
16 IOW town (4)
18 Beard of cereal (3)
20 French composer (7)
21 Line touching curve (7)
23 Prophet consulted (6)
24 'Ship of the desert' (5)
25 Not in good shape (5)
27 Snake (5)
29 Attempt (3)

46

Across

1 *Extract money from* (4)
4 *Arab leader* (6)
7 Crazy person (3)
9 Eye inflammation (4)
10 Motor for boat (8)
11 Honourable title (3)
12 Charity (4)
13 Fictional ape (4,4)
16 Cranefly larva (13)
19 Neolithic tool (5,3)
23 Group of actors (4)
24 Large vessel (3)
25 Obsolete coin (8)
26 Of many colours (4)
27 Garland of flowers (3)
28 Morally pure (6)
29 Military vehicle (4)

Down

2 Brainy person (12)
3 Israeli parliament (7)
4 Long-legged bird (5)
5 Taken as food (5)
6 Small stall (5)
8 Monster's creator (12)
14 Glasgow football ground (5)
15 Indian resort (3)
17 Garden tool (3)
18 Racing driver's seat (7)
20 Indentation (5)
21 Alternative name (5)
22 Bird of prey (5)

47

Across

1 *Gasp* (4)
4 *Assam, for instance* (3)
6 *Garden tools* (4)
8 Improvement (6)
9 Fall over (6)
10 Feeler (8)
11 Body of a church (4)
12 Lingerie (13)
17 Traverse swiftly (4)
19 Spar at front of ship (8)
22 Skilful (6)
23 One who's hooked (6)
24 Singlet (4)
25 Plaything (3)
26 Public garden (4)

Down

2 Large enough (5)
3 Property manager (7)
4 Pick-me-up (5)
5 Redcoat (anag.) (3,4)
6 Mortal (5)
7 Excite (7)
10 19th Greek letter (3)
13 Aircraft body (7)
14 Bear cat (anag.) (7)
15 Stimulated (5,2)
16 Intestine (3)
18 Sod (5)
20 Tired (5)
21 Suffer (5)

48

Across

1 *Correct; formal* (6)
4 *Male goose* (6)
7 Stringed percussion instrument (8)
9 Half man, half horse (7)
12 Vision (5)
13 Internal (5)
15 Proportion, relation (5)
16 Book of maps (5)
17 Wanderer (5)
18 Offspring; topic (5)
19 Perplex (7)
23 Wakeful (8)
24 Alter (6)
25 Made speeches (6)

Down

1 Walker; prosaic (10)
2 Duty (10)
3 Expulsion (8)
4 Impale (4)
5 Tidy (4)
6 Jacob's twin brother (4)
8 Scrimp (9)
10 Teenager (10)
11 Calculated again (10)
14 Heater — or cooler! (8)
20 Curse (4)
21 Scheme (4)
22 Induce; yearning (4)

The Telegraph

49

Across

1 *Agree* (7)
8 *Seaman; class* (6)
9 Began; flinched (7)
11 Abandoned (8)
12 Choosy (5)
14 Responsibility (4)
15 Stir dust (anag.) (8)
17 Forceful (8)
18 Embargo (4)
20 Loaded (5)
21 Munificent; liberal (8)
23 Layer (7)
24 Number; team (6)
25 Adjective (7)

Down

2 Overtake, escape (6)
3 Emphasis (6)
4 Want (4)
5 Splendour (7)
6 Mocked (9)
7 Commotion (9)
10 Tasty (9)
12 Alien (9)
13 Postponed; hung (9)
16 Wed (7)
18 Empty (6)
19 Occupancy (6)
22 Pace (4)

50

Across

1 *Tailback* (5)
4 *Beast* (5)
8 Nominate (7)
9 Wrath (5)
10 Recreational complex (7,6)
11 Australian city (6)
12 Vegetable (6)
15 Reassurance (13)
18 European capital (5)
19 Himalayan mountain (7)
20 Plucked instrument (5)
21 Put off (5)

Down

1 Game bird (5)
2 Group loyalty (6,2,5)
3 Gourmet (7)
4 Male servant (6)
5 Custom (5)
6 Lively dance (9,4)
7 Pressing (6)
11 Drowsy (6)
13 Make believe (7)
14 Vocation (6)
16 Distress (5)
17 Shabby (5)

The Telegraph

51

Across

1 *Brag* (5)
4 *Twist forcibly* (5)
8 Stormed (7)
9 Midday meal (5)
10 A four-sided figure (13)
11 Religious house (6)
12 City in Texas (6)
15 Racehorse (13)
18 Happening (5)
19 Advance showing (7)
20 Herb (5)
21 Hard wood (5)

Down

1 Airship (5)
2 Commercial (13)
3 Young child (7)
4 Beer-can device (6)
5 Inuit house (5)
6 Supreme commander (13)
7 English river (6)
11 Zodiac sign (6)
13 Sportsman (7)
14 Persons in general (6)
16 Small-minded (5)
17 Noisy (5)

52

Across

1 *Atmosphere* (4)
3 *Curt* (5)
7 Wild goat (4)
8 Inadvertent (10)
9 Singing voice (4)
12 Root vegetable (5,6)
13 Madrid museum (5)
15 Engine (5)
19 Unending (11)
21 Whirlpool (4)
23 Stage promoter (10)
24 Cereal food (4)
25 Italian port (5)
26 Jibes (4)

Down

1 Lump in throat (5,5)
2 Eased in (anag) (7)
3 Idiots! (6)
4 Revolve (6)
5 Israeli resort (5)
6 Rhythm (4)
10 Attic (4)
11 Exorbitant (10)
14 Made redundant (4)
16 External (7)
17 Visit (4,2)
18 Photographer's kit (6)
20 Competing (5)
22 Dagger (4)

The Telegraph

53

Across

1 *Lack* (4)
4 *Academics* (4)
8 *Circular band* (4)
9 Unaltered state (6,3)
11 Pregnant (6)
13 Annual book (7)
15 Minor (6)
16 Hunger (6)
18 Root vegetable (6)
20 Slight wind (6)
22 Fleets (7)
23 Tell (6)
25 Operative (9)
26 Drunken revelry (4)
27 Show off (4)
28 A length (4)

Down

2 Stake (4)
3 Adds up (6)
4 Ban (6)
5 Nutty sweet (6)
6 Talks (9)
7 Potato (4)
10 Fruit garden (7)
12 Hole for money (4)
13 Star divination (9)
14 Arbitrate (7)
17 Row; level (4)
19 Favour (6)
20 Scoundrel (3,3)
21 Coarse (6)
23 Space (4)
24 State (4)

54

Across

1 *Automobile* (3)
3 *Silent* (3)
5 *Naked* (4)
7 Heaps (5)
8 Inhabit (6)
10 Squad (4)
11 Upstanding (8)
13 Ointment (6)
14 Infer (6)
17 United (8)
19 Prejudice (4)
21 Starvation (6)
22 Complete (5)
23 Formerly (4)
24 Plaything (3)
25 Rug (3)

Down

1 Surrender (10)
2 Dependent (7)
3 Interlock (4)
4 Ghoulish (6)
5 Smitten (8)
6 Wireless (5)
9 Evaluation (10)
12 Repentant (8)
15 Outfit (7)
16 Flaw (6)
18 Seed (5)
20 Influence (4)

The Telegraph

55

Across

1 *Stuffing, say* (6)
4 *Large beer mugs* (6)
9 Power (5)
10 Enlarged (7)
11 Consume (3)
12 Say (5)
13 More worked up (7)
15 Caloric unit (anag.) (11)
19 Areas (7)
20 Piercing (5)
21 Amateur radio operator (3)
22 Fancy (7)
24 Mediterranean tree (5)
25 Car storage area (6)
26 Restrained (6)

Down

1 Well-known (6)
2 Atmospheric discharge (9)
3 Go in (5)
5 Idea (7)
6 Poorly (3)
7 Guard (6)
8 He is baldest (anag.) (11)
14 Solitude (9)
16 Finishing (7)
17 Attempting (6)
18 Scatter (6)
20 Fumes (5)
23 Aura (3)

56

Across

1 *Baronet's title* (3)
3 *Intrude* (3)
5 *Celebrate* (4)
7 Target area (5)
8 Not solid or gas (6)
10 Nasty child (4)
11 Holding together (8)
13 Probable (6)
14 Skin complaint (6)
17 Saying little (8)
19 — Gagarin, cosmonaut (4)
21 Opinion (6)
22 Unclothed people (5)
23 Scoff (4)
24 Present container? (3)
25 Shaft of light (3)

Down

1 Catchword, slogan (10)
2 Loot (7)
3 Unadulterated (4)
4 Cowardly (6)
5 Succession (8)
6 Simple-minded (5)
9 Russian composer (10)
12 Seller of garments (8)
15 South American country (7)
16 Temporary building (6)
18 Mediterranean island (5)
20 Semi-precious stone (4)

57

Across

1 *Chop* (3)
3 *Principally* (6)
7 Tyros (7)
8 Exposition ending QED? (5)
10 Seductive woman (4)
11 Joyful (8)
13 Newspaper article (6)
15 Dog (6)
17 Young in style (8)
18 False god (4)
21 Less wet (5)
22 Earth/sky interface (7)
23 Female monster (6)
24 Receptacle (3)

Down

1 Harbour (5)
2 Candle component (4)
3 Place of worship (6)
4 Put in jail (8)
5 Wild cat (7)
6 Out of work (10)
9 Country of origin (10)
12 Marine fish (3,5)
14 Funny (7)
16 Woody plants (6)
19 Set of 12 (5)
20 Larva; food (4)

58

Across

1 *Henry (diminutive)* (3)
3 *Free* (5)
6 *Err* (3)
8 *Of a continent* (5)
9 Saw choc (anag.); steady investment (4,3)
10 Stupid act (10)
12 Hit (colloq.) (3)
15 Discretion (4)
17 Retain (4)
18 Gear (3)
22 Rewarding (10)
25 Poison (7)
26 Tartan cloth (5)
27 Plaything (3)
28 Discover (3,2)
29 Flop (3)

Down

1 Spring flower (8)
2 Easy-going (4-4)
3 Foolishness (6)
4 Mystical (6)
5 Imitation (6)
6 Short stocking (4)
7 Tailed amphibian (4)
11 Asian ox (3)
13 Bad grope (anag.); scoring gadget (8)
14 Superb (8)
16 End (3)
19 Ditch (6)
20 Remnant (6)
21 Stay at home (4,2)
23 Huge (4)
24 Detect (4)

59

Across

1 *Bank order* (6)
4 *Thickened milk* (4)
9 *Asian territory, two countries* (5)
10 Exact copy (7)
11 Projecting outwards; significant (7)
12 Praise highly (5)
13 Untidy place (6)
15 Concealed gunman (6)
18 Hooded snake (5)
20 Organised criminal (7)
23 Small pamphlet (7)
24 Hanger-on (5)
25 Lie in wait (4)
26 Baby's footwear (6)

Down

1 Covers in e.g. mud (5)
2 Noise excluder (7)
3 Authoritarian decree (5)
5 Indefinite number (7)
6 General meaning (5)
7 Great anger (5)
8 Garment maker (6)
13 Difficult situation (6)
14 Fishing boat (7)
16 Plan of work (7)
17 Express feelings (5)
19 Unruly fight (5)
21 Page number (5)
22 Yellow pigment (5)

60

Across

1 *Window glass* (4)
3 *Post; wager* (5)
7 *Monarch* (4)
8 Provisional divorce document (6,4)
9 Christmas (4)
12 Footwear laces (11)
13 Course (5)
15 Pain, torment (5)
19 Promising, optimistic (11)
21 Roman emperor (4)
23 Surgical transfer (10)
24 Flat round plate (4)
25 Rambler (5)
26 Snow runners (4)

Down

1 Walker (10)
2 Serious (7)
3 Afternoon nap (6)
4 Sharp, sour (6)
5 Managing to make (a living) (5)
6 At one time (4)
10 Norwegian capital (4)
11 Inflammation of the vocal cords (10)
14 Consumer (4)
16 Eye-protectors (7)
17 (N Amer.) Indian (6)
18 Rubber (6)
20 Cut (5)
22 Way out (4)

61

Across

1 *Trapped* (6)
7 *Arrange; senior officer* (7)
8 Replied (8)
9 Fortunate (5)
10 Citrus fruit (5)
11 The first man (4)
12 Striped animal (5)
15 Rot (5)
16 Blockade (5)
19 Reverberate (4)
20 Moral (5)
21 Stench (5)
22 Very hot curry (8)
23 Local, indigenous (7)
24 Deviate (6)

Down

1 Negligent (8)
2 Final (8)
3 Wading bird (5)
4 Father (3)
5 Suppose (6)
6 Pedestrian (6)
7 Glum (11)
9 Idle (4)
13 Unmarried man (8)
14 Story (8)
15 Adorn; pack (cards) (4)
17 Focused (6)
18 Sex (6)
20 Bequeath (5)
22 By way of (3)

62

Across

1 *Wharf* (4)
3 *Clever scheme* (6)
9 Try (7)
10 Cereal plant (5)
11 Untruth (3)
12 London suburb (9)
13 Clown (6)
14 Leisurely walk (6)
16 Henry —, US diplomat (9)
19 Soft fruit (3)
21 Tree, copper — (5)
22 Ignorant (7)
23 'Kubla Khan' city (6)
24 Prepare for publication (4)

Down

1 Game bird (5)
2 Without guile (7)
4 Compassionate (12)
5 Live (5)
6 Endless (7)
7 Poor (12)
8 Halt (4)
13 Nickelodeon (7)
15 Casual (7)
17 Ship's rear (5)
18 Surplus (4)
20 Considerable (5)

The Telegraph

63

Across

1 *Painter of seascapes* (6)
5 *Consider* (5)
9 Open-mindedness (9)
10 Friend (3)
11 Cashew, for example (3)
12 Forsaken (9)
14 Opening (3)
16 Prize (5)
18 Cambridgeshire city (3)
19 Like a gymnast (9)
21 Health resort (3)
22 Pig (3)
23 Benefit (9)
25 Scope (5)
26 Chaos (6)

Down

2 Not illuminated (5)
3 Paradise (7)
4 Sprint (3)
5 Brandish (5)
6 Encroach (7)
7 Tourist (12)
8 Court employee (12)
13 Modify (5)
15 Perfect example (7)
17 Propriety (7)
20 Pair (5)
21 No longer fresh (5)
24 Energy (3)

Across

1 *Sound of regret* (4)
4 *Faults* (7)
8 Recollect (8)
9 Suffer (3)
11 Gift (6)
13 Gaming club (6)
14 Question hard (5)
15 Merit (4)
17 Kind (4)
18 Dismal (5)
20 Gismo (6)
21 Hidden (6)
24 Mythical bird (3)
25 Introduction (8)
26 Watered down (7)
27 Front of plane (4)

Down

2 Perfect (5)
3 Weeding (6)
4 Fingerprints (sl.) (4)
5 Ceremonial (6)
6 Help for needy (7)
7 Outline (10)
10 Place that's beyond reality (10)
12 Characteristic (5)
13 Wooden shoes (5)
16 Revolutionary (7)
18 Autocrat (6)
19 Beefeater (6)
22 Annoys (5)
23 Conflict (4)

65

Across

1 *Star* (3)
3 *High* (4)
5 *Small rolls* (4)
8 Declare (8)
10 Profound (4)
11 American fuel (3)
13 Of ebbs and flows (5)
14 Writing skin (9)
16 Beer (3)
17 Grannie (3)
19 Barrage (9)
21 Obvious (5)
22 Pitch (3)
24 Agony (4)
25 Murder (8)
26 Dispatched (4)
27 Yield (4)
28 Rugby score (3)

Down

1 Male deer (4)
2 Sisters (4)
3 Police clubs (10)
4 Find (6)
6 Everlasting (8)
7 Replace (8)
9 Of birth (5)
12 Fetching; cute (10)
14 Wind instrument (3-5)
15 Family member (8)
18 In front (5)
20 Walked (6)
22 Lean; joust (4)
23 Bank (on) (4)

The Telegraph

66

Across

1 *Whinny* (5)
4 *Tease* (3)
6 *Indeed* (3)
8 Fitness training (13)
9 Symbol (5)
11 Cereal (4)
13 Scoffed (5)
14 Bleeper (5)
15 Multitude (5)
16 Advantage (4)
18 Popular flowers (5)
21 Oxbridge college (6,7)
23 Chum (3)
24 Roll (3)
25 Perhaps (5)

Down

1 Drink of the gods (6)
2 Work-shy (4)
3 Raise (5)
4 Equipment (3)
5 Idealist (7)
6 Het up (8)
7 Flag (6)
10 Roman garments (5)
12 NCO (8)
14 Bother (7)
15 Snag (6)
17 Tax (6)
19 Inoculation liquid (5)
20 Catch sight of (4)
22 Policeman (3)

67

Across

1 *Snoop* (3)
3 *Healthy* (3)
5 *Tall* (4)
7 Quaffed (5)
8 Haphazard (6)
10 Rational (4)
11 Callous (8)
13 Conundrum (6)
14 Dumbfound (6)
17 Irregular (8)
19 Deficit (4)
21 Passion (6)
22 Nimble (5)
23 Jumble (4)
24 Sever (3)
25 Fiery (3)

Down

1 Walker (10)
2 Longed (7)
3 Counterfeit (4)
4 Steamy (6)
5 Obstacle (8)
6 Earth (5)
9 Estimation (10)
12 Illustrious (8)
15 Absurd (7)
16 Material (6)
18 Courage (5)
20 Tirade (4)

68

Across

7 *Recorded votes of* (6)
8 *Reply* (6)
10 Arthur's capital (7)
11 Group of twelve (5)
12 Base for sauce (4)
13 Part of act (5)
17 Contend against (5)
18 Desire (4)
22 Type of pigeon (5)
23 Varnish (7)
24 Smoothly (in music) (6)
25 European country (6)

Down

1 Ghost (7)
2 Glitz (7)
3 Solid dessert (5)
4 Dull and inoffensive (7)
5 Mild swindle (5)
6 Tree stem (5)
9 Swedish city (9)
14 Quiver (7)
15 Road surfacing (7)
16 Smoothie (7)
19 Huge mammal (5)
20 Picture (5)
21 Total of points (5)

The Telegraph

69

Across

1 *Interjection of disgust* (3)
3 *Merriment* (3)
5 *Horror* (5)
8 New (5)
9 Autobiography? (7)
10 US university (4)
11 Thirst-destroying drink (8)
13 Cartoon bear (6)
14 Physical damage (6)
17 Very attentive to wife (8)
19 *See 6 Down*
22 Current-measurer (7)
23 Erroneous (5)
24 – Army, cricket supporters (5)
25 School of Buddhism (3)
26 Female religious (3)

Down

1 Imagine (5)
2 Enclose (7)
3 People (4)
4 Cloud (6)
5 Soh in scale (8)
6 & 19 Across 'Little Sparrow' (5,4)
7 Demolish (7)
12 Skill (8)
13 Edible stalks (7)
15 Lion's adversary (7)
16 Glassy mineral (6)
18 Shell (5)
20 Dickens villain (5)
21 Graceful bird (4)

Across

1 *Harvest season* (6)
5 *Room at the top* (5)
9 Expressing delight (9)
10 Pastry dish (3)
11 Take to court (3)
12 Large seabird (9)
14 Priestly garment (3)
16 Subject to prohibition (5)
18 Current unit (3)
19 Professional driver (9)
21 Coniferous tree (3)
22 Take food (3)
23 Twin-hulled boat (9)
25 Enigmatic representation (5)
26 Straw hat (6)

Down

2 Habitual practice (5)
3 Nouveau-riche (7)
4 Lower the head (3)
5 Berkshire racecourse (5)
6 Milk pudding ingredient (7)
7 Penny-pinching (12)
8 Easy to understand (7,5)
13 Authoritative source (5)
15 Lucky dip (4,3)
17 Crew member (7)
20 Centre of attention (5)
21 Meeting place (5)
24 Useful suggestion (3)

The Telegraph

71

Across

1 *Adjudicator* (5)
4 *Denoted* (5)
8 *Pointed tool* (3)
9 Before written records (11)
10 Matrimonial (7)
12 Condescend (5)
13 A guy, for instance (6)
14 Jury (Scotland) (6)
17 Fragile (5)
19 Endless (7)
21 One with severe doubts (11)
23 Signal (3)
24 Verse (5)
25 Bring (5)

Down

1 Far Eastern country (5)
2 Female rabbit (3)
3 Leaving (7)
4 Courage (6)
5 Pungent (5)
6 Skilful mover (9)
7 Tel Edna (anag.); firm to bite (2,5)
11 African viper (4,5)
13 Impose (7)
15 Chief officer (7)
16 Decree (anag.) (6)
18 Robust (5)
20 Conifer (5)
22 Tank (3)

72

Across

1 *Rule* (5)
4 *Bill of exchange* (6)
9 Bewilder (7)
10 Florida resort (5)
11 Welsh emblem (4)
12 Middle; crucial (7)
13 Protrude (3)
14 Fete (4)
16 Converse (4)
18 Snoop (3)
20 Gruesome (7)
21 Notion (4)
24 Curse (5)
25 Happy (7)
26 Waver (6)
27 Name for a parrot (5)

Down

1 Lottery (6)
2 Accustom (5)
3 Title (4)
5 People; kindness (8)
6 Argument (7)
7 Eatable (6)
8 Precise (5)
13 Scouts' rally (8)
15 Antique (7)
17 Entertained (6)
18 Serenity (5)
19 Food store (6)
22 Reside (5)
23 Break; photo (4)

73

Across

1 *Royal chair* (6)
4 *Finished; above* (4)
9 *Wearied* (5)
10 Asian fruit (7)
11 Surrounding (7)
12 Idealised prose (5)
13 Shrewd (6)
15 Kinsman (6)
18 Clear (5)
20 Theft (7)
23 Fervent (7)
24 Evade (5)
25 Pace (4)
26 Awful (6)

Down

1 Shinbone (5)
2 Cheese/toast savoury (7)
3 Jostle (5)
5 Dizziness (7)
6 Stony; unsteady (5)
7 Celebration (5)
8 Purloined (6)
13 On fire (6)
14 Young frog (7)
16 Slim (7)
17 Near; shut (5)
19 Disorder (5)
21 Wireless (5)
22 Submit (5)

74

Across

1 *Joint* (4)
5 *Cloy* (4)
7 Sugared almond (7)
8 Stocky (8)
10 Suspect (4)
12 Eagerly excited (4)
14 Come to be lacking (3,5)
16 Box (8)
17 Harvest (4)
18 Front of jaw (4)
19 Edge of wharf (8)
22 Cheat (7)
23 Disorder (4)
24 Clever (4)

Down

1 German philosopher (4)
2 Large-scale (4)
3 Ancient language (8)
4 Assembly (4)
5 Nuisance (8)
6 Flower (4)
9 Nonsense (7)
11 Presumptuous (7)
13 Dismal quality (8)
15 French area (8)
18 Tranquil (4)
19 Off-the-cuff joke (4)
20 Cast off (4)
21 Leave (4)

The Telegraph

75

Across

1 *Squander* (5)
3 *Forbidden* (6)
7 Wanton damage (9)
9 Instinct (4)
10 Expression (4)
11 Protective garment (5)
13 Obtain wrongfully (6)
14 Nervous (5)
15 Misery (5)
17 Football (6)
20 Vehicle (5)
21 Prohibit (4)
23 Rebuff (4)
24 Pleasure (9)
25 Arizona city (6)
26 Alacrity (5)

Down

1 Battered cake (6)
2 Duck (4)
3 Great wave (6)
4 Set of tables (4)
5 Play (5)
6 Modify; acclimatise (5)
7 Expose to air (9)
8 Beggar (9)
11 Missile (5)
12 US president (5)
16 Brownish crimson (6)
17 French river (5)
18 Coarse (6)
19 US tennis player (5)
22 Burden (4)
23 Bargain (4)

76

Across

1 *Grab* (5)
4 *Conceal* (4)
7 Clutch (4)
8 Normal (8)
9 Lively (9)
10 Gamble (3)
12 Antenna (6)
14 Complete (6)
16 Expert (3)
18 Desecration (9)
21 Profusion (8)
22 Part of eye (4)
23 Bulk large (4)
24 Therefore (5)

Down

1 Weird (7)
2 Jeopardises (8)
3 Wear away (5)
4 Chase (4)
5 Lament (5)
6 Counsel (6)
11 Horse (8)
13 Logic (6)
15 Form of jazz (7)
17 String instrument (5)
19 Extent (5)
20 Particle (4)

77

Across

1 *Cloak, wrap* (5)
5 *Pull hard* (5)
8 Love (5)
9 Frequently (5)
10 Tall podge (anag.) (4,5)
11 In addition (3)
12 Off-the-peg (5-2-4)
15 Disposition (11)
19 Shack (3)
20 Fill again (9)
22 Deport (5)
23 Spicy sauce (5)
24 Peanut sauce (5)
25 Frock (5)

Down

1 Quicker way (5,3)
2 Writer (6)
3 Tongue (8)
4 Miscellaneous (6)
5 Pile (4)
6 Covered passage (6)
7 Sharpness (4)
13 Business cost (8)
14 Agitated (8)
16 Little darling (6)
17 With keenness (6)
18 Three times (6)
20 Deep furrows (4)
21 Simple (4)

The Telegraph

78

Across

1 *Crucial* (3)
3 *Dispatched* (4)
5 *Hades* (4)
8 Afflicted (8)
10 Miserly (4)
11 Star (3)
13 Domain (5)
14 Chief (9)
16 Age (3)
17 Tin (3)
19 Brain (9)
21 Gloss (5)
22 Cover (3)
24 Grade (4)
25 Adventure (8)
26 Boring (4)
27 Worry (4)
28 Decay (3)

Down

1 Peck (4)
2 Tale (4)
3 Sugary (10)
4 Required (6)
6 Refinement (8)
7 Lotion (8)
9 Coach (5)
12 Immaterial (10)
14 Expurgated (8)
15 Motherly (8)
18 Pungent (5)
20 Puzzle (6)
22 Den (4)
23 Arrears (4)

The Telegraph

79

Across

1 *Inferior* (5)
4 *Killed* (5)
8 Operate (3)
9 Patriot (11)
10 Abode (7)
12 Grab (5)
13 Crave (6)
14 Stick (6)
17 Colossus (5)
19 Lengthen (7)
21 Deceitful (11)
23 Owed (3)
24 Shufti (5)
25 Blunder (5)

Down

1 Hang (5)
2 Damp (3)
3 Cock (7)
4 Meagre (6)
5 Pseudonym (5)
6 Food (9)
7 Assuage (7)
11 Onlooker (9)
13 Humiliate (7)
15 Beloved (7)
16 Hope (6)
18 Subject (5)
20 Speed (5)
22 Rotten (3)

The Telegraph

80

Across

1 *Bash* (5)
4 *Seabirds* (5)
8 Fuss (3)
9 Without compromise (4-7)
10 Break from meeting (7)
12 Acclaim (5)
13 Public square (6)
14 Grave (6)
17 Bird's perch (5)
19 Betrothed (7)
21 Wind-controlled instrument (7,4)
23 Go wrong (3)
24 Part of Mass (5)
25 Body in space (5)

Down

1 Czech novelist (5)
2 Bird (3)
3 Israeli community (7)
4 Covered in spikes (6)
5 Elevated strip (5)
6 Cyclist's container (9)
7 Canadian police officer (7)
11 French heroine (4,2,3)
13 Floor covering (7)
15 Derived from living matter (7)
16 Country adjoining USA (6)
18 Treasure store (5)
20 Storehouse (5)
22 Limb (3)

The Telegraph

81

Across

1 *Less well* (6)
4 *Ornamented* (5)
8 Fire (5)
9 Present (7)
10 Less heavy (7)
11 Printing error (4)
12 Garden location (3)
14 Therefore (4)
15 Lasso? (4)
18 Small drink (3)
21 Fortune (4)
23 Travelling bags etc (7)
25 Notes (7)
26 Jumped (5)
27 Devoid of content (5)
28 Author (6)

Down

1 Not 'in your face' (6)
2 Dish; horse (7)
3 Effort (8)
4 Solid nourishment (4)
5 Fine (slang) (5)
6 Herb (6)
7 Electrical discharge (5)
13 Fidgety person (8)
16 Country labourer (7)
17 Exclusive group (6)
19 Luxurious (5)
20 Court joker? (6)
22 Muscular contraction (5)
24 Tax (4)

The Telegraph

82

Across

1 *Churchyard tree* (3)
3 *Leg joint* (4)
5 *Paul –, Swiss surrealist* (4)
8 The roast (anag.); electrical instrument (8)
10 Glaswegian? (4)
11 Yikes! Oo-er! (3)
13 Pierce (5)
14 Necessarily (9)
16 Pub (3)
17 I (3)
19 Desire to travel (5,4)
21 Sorrow (5)
22 Inquire (3)
24 Notion (4)
25 Rice dish (8)
26 Pierce (4)
27 Confront (4)
28 Lair (3)

Down

1 Yesteryear (4)
2 Seven days (4)
3 Artificial respiration (4,2,4)
4 Glossy coating (6)
6 Publican (8)
7 Storehouse (8)
9 Trojan beauty (5)
12 Transitory (3-2-5)
14 Annoying slightly (8)
15 Contrive (8)
18 Web-footed birds (5)
20 Stilton (6)
22 Parched (4)
23 Avid (4)

83

Across

1 *Dance playfully* (5)
4 *Irish night out* (7)
8 Animal fodder (3)
9 Hot alcoholic drink (5)
10 Mischievous spirit (7)
11 One whose talent is overlooked (10)
14 Quagmire (6)
16 Powerful businessman (6)
18 Cherry liqueur (10)
22 Very surprising (7)
23 Quantity of e.g. eggs (5)
24 Shelter (3)
25 Ancestry (7)
26 Fictional otter (5)

Down

1 Burial place (8)
2 Over-attention to detail (8)
3 Sound correspondence (5)
4 Young swan (6)
5 In the perfect case (7)
6 Not working (4)
7 Loop of yarn (4)
12 Trench mortar (8)
13 Inability to sleep (8)
15 Staying power (7)
17 Obtain craftily (6)
19 Trainee soldier (5)
20 Flexible armour (4)
21 Cultivated grass (4)

84

Across

4 *Lumberjack* (6)
5 *Portion* (4)
7 Cringed (7)
10 Agog (5)
11 Trusting (7)
12 Male singer (5)
14 Height (7)
15 Dust-coloured (5)
16 Malady (7)
20 Name (5)
21 Queen of the Fairies (7)
22 Pitcher (4)
23 Soft-surfaced fabric (6)

Down

1 Change (5)
2 Gem (5)
3 Sea cow (7)
4 Lash (4)
6 Shudder; quake (6)
8 Cold-blooded vertebrate (7)
9 Remote (7)
10 Confide (7)
13 Selection (6)
14 Expert, adroit (7)
17 Sea duck (5)
18 Volley (5)
19 Catalogue; tilt (4)

85

Across

1 *Bronze coin* (5)
4 *Tight* (5)
10 Normal (7)
11 Alarm; temptress (5)
12 Freight (5)
13 Russian tea-urn (7)
15 Second-hand (4)
17 Lariat (5)
19 In good time (5)
22 Discover (4)
25 Calendar (7)
27 New World parrot (5)
29 Woo; tribunal (5)
30 Relate (7)
31 Series (5)
32 Jungle mammal; laziness (5)

Down

2 Come in (5)
3 Fearful (7)
5 Derby racecourse (5)
6 Wither (7)
7 Light meal (5)
8 Nearby (5)
9 Irate (5)
14 Yemen port (4)
16 Couch (4)
18 Arsenal (7)
20 Senior naval officer (7)
21 Tally; game (5)
23 Sugar-coating (5)
24 Proprietor (5)
26 Of one's birth (5)
28 Map (5)

86

Across

1 *Complain peevishly* (5)
4 *Seaweed* (5)
8 Brush (7)
9 Hog's-back (5)
10 Diversion (13)
11 Complete (6)
12 Churlish (6)
15 Prevaricate (3,2,3,5)
18 Web-footed birds (5)
19 Rice dish (7)
20 Subject (5)
21 Filthy (5)

Down

1 Squander (5)
2 A crime of personal fraud (8,5)
3 Ruler (7)
4 Capital of Poland (6)
5 Pinafore (5)
6 Town on the Stour (13)
7 Guard (6)
11 Flag (6)
13 Declined (7)
14 Price (6)
16 Female relative (5)
17 A hard wood (5)

87

Across

1 *Effervescent* (5)
4 *Blister-like sacs* (5)
8 Montmartre painter, 1883–1955 (7)
9 Elk (5)
10 Insect (7,6)
11 In heaven (2,4)
12 Up-to-date (6)
15 American short-story writer (5,5,3)
18 Energy (5)
19 Head waiter (6,1)
20 Pool of money (5)
21 Lowest point (5)

Down

1 Dowdy woman (5)
2 1964 film starring Anthony Quinn (5,3,5)
3 Bellowing (7)
4 Bird in crow family (6)
5 Brazilian dance (5)
6 Easily moved to anger (5-8)
7 Cause (6)
11 Alternatively (2,4)
13 Applause (7)
14 Ham-fisted (6)
16 Terms of reference (5)
17 Sea duck (5)

88

Across

1 *Tray* (6)
4 *Threshold* (4)
9 *Linger* (5)
10 Go away! (3,4)
11 Letter (7)
12 Burial chamber (5)
13 Flock of geese (6)
15 Explosions (6)
18 Kingdom (5)
20 Entrails (7)
23 Instalment (7)
24 Commander (5)
25 Medal (4)
26 Explanation (6)

Down

1 Move furtively (5)
2 Calming (7)
3 Arab republic (5)
5 Visual (7)
6 Spacious (5)
7 Correspond (5)
8 Standing (6)
13 Attic (6)
14 Mock (7)
16 Extra (7)
17 Quoted (5)
19 Parroting (5)
21 Hospital worker (5)
22 Warning signal (5)

The Telegraph

89

Across

1 *Authorise; overtake* (4)
3 *Seat* (5)
7 *Views* (4)
8 Leaving (10)
9 Copies (4)
12 For a while (11)
13 Fathered (5)
15 Pancake (5)
19 Cool (manner) (11)
21 Spanish painter (4)
23 Cheat by copying; agile pairs (anag.) (10)
24 Comfort (4)
25 Types (5)
26 Evils (4)

Down

1 Rehearsing (10)
2 Nerve junction (7)
3 Groups of singers (6)
4 Bird sanctuary (6)
5 Majestic (5)
6 Yield (4)
10 Funeral fire (4)
11 Struck dumb (10)
14 Optimistic (4)
16 Changes (7)
17 Not just (6)
18 Imitates (6)
20 Records (5)
22 Spoken (4)

The Telegraph

90

Across

1 *End of sock* (3)
3 *Stall* (5)
6 *Impair* (3)
8 *Strength* (5)
9 Start of match (4-3)
10 Old-fashioned greeting (3,2,3,2)
12 Newt (3)
15 Tuft (4)
17 Amphibious neighbour of 12? (4)
18 Moose-like deer (3)
22 Former European republic (10)
25 Fuel supply (3,4)
26 Welsh dog breed (5)
27 Go wrong (3)
28 Hot alcoholic drink (5)
29 Eternity (3)

Down

1 War-axe (8)
2 Sideways (8)
3 TV comedy (6)
4 Demand (3,3)
5 The noughties, say (6)
6 Disposition (4)
7 Split (4)
11 Rancid (3)
13 Cross (8)
14 Relating to land (8)
16 Work at (3)
19 Oil-rich country (6)
20 With outgrowths on head (6)
21 Courageous (6)
23 Monster (4)
24 Russian emperor (4)

The Telegraph

91

Across

1 *Part of curve* (3)
3 *Container* (3)
5 *Wound; painful* (4)
7 Astonish (5)
8 Faction (6)
10 Blow (4)
11 Nepalese capital (alt. spelling) (8)
13 Assemble (6)
14 Shrewd (6)
17 Hitchcock film (3,5)
19 Greek god (4)
21 Rarely found (6)
22 Greek letter (5)
23 Swiss painter (4)
24 Belly (3)
25 Miserable (3)

Down

1 Merge (10)
2 Car framework (7)
3 Head cook (4)
4 Drink of gods (6)
5 Minor fight (8)
6 French city (5)
9 Australian state (10)
12 Stock (8)
15 Futile (7)
16 Swedish tennis player (6)
18 Surpass (5)
20 Shock (4)

92

Across

1 *Watch* (5)
4 *Female relations* (7)
8 Peculiar (3)
9 Auction item (3)
10 Disney character (5)
11 Additional (5)
12 Darling (7)
15 PC memory unit (4)
17 Photo problem (3-3)
19 Job making money (6)
22 Accept (4)
24 Wild primula (7)
26 Royal Indian male (5)
28 Pool of players (5)
30 Idle chat (3)
31 An infection (3)
32 Not hypocritical (7)
33 Let (5)

Down

1 Dutch painter (7)
2 Scale (5)
3 Cradle song (7)
4 Give evidence (of) (6)
5 Peer (5)
6 Belief system (3)
7 Grab (5)
13 Seven days (4)
14 100 mph (3)
16 Mythical snowman (4)
18 Condensation (3)
20 A suspension (7)
21 Put in new home (7)
23 Satellite's furthest point (6)
24 Barrels (5)
25 Shelf (5)
27 Orange (5)
29 Ashes trophy (3)

The Telegraph

93

Across

1 *Draw through straw?* (4)
4 *Sitting* (7)
8 Fabric (8)
9 Farm animal (3)
11 Berthing area (6)
13 Tomb of saint? (6)
14 Form of oxygen (5)
15 Cook's thickening (4)
17 Cure, recover (4)
18 Direction indicator (5)
20 European river (6)
21 Trafalgar Square bird? (6)
24 And not (3)
25 Stringed instruments (8)
26 Tallest mountain ... (7)
27 ... and creature supposedly there (4)

Down

2 Helper at wedding (5)
3 Japanese robe (6)
4 Froth of wave (4)
5 Cutting tool (6)
6 Slope (7)
7 Country (3,7)
10 Injudiciousness (10)
12 Shade of blue (5)
13 Spy (5)
16 Disconcert (7)
18 Disavow (6)
19 Drink-making establishment (6)
22 Choose by voting (5)
23 Depart, resign from (4)

The Telegraph

94

Across

1 *Tooth (facetious)* (7)
5 *Not valid* (4)
7 *Bundle up* (5)
8 Take in (6)
10 Long seat (4)
11 Merrymaker (8)
13 Building adhesive (6)
14 Pacific islanders' garment (6)
17 Drug often smoked (8)
19 Martial art (4)
21 Red gemstone (6)
22 Tearful (5)
23 Make keen (4)
24 Item of chemists' equipment (7)

Down

1 Site of Jesus's arrest (10)
2 Water source (7)
3 Army; publican (4)
4 Utterly destroyed (6)
5 Male aristocrat (8)
6 Descriptive tag (5)
9 Cave-dweller (10)
12 Strict disciplinarian (8)
15 Very rich (7)
16 Arch of foot (6)
18 Be incompatible (5)
20 Exchange (4)

The Telegraph

95

Across

1 *Health resort* (3)
3 *Monarch* (4)
5 *Stopper* (4)
8 WWI (5,3)
10 Burden (4)
11 Coal-scuttle (3)
13 Shadow (5)
14 Nepal's mountains (9)
16 Undivided (3)
17 Beer (3)
19 Imposed (9)
21 Old Peruvian (5)
22 Maria ___ Duarte De Perón (3)
24 Zing (4)
25 More nauseous (8)
26 Roster (4)
27 Cattle-shed (4)
28 Light-hearted (3)

Down

1 Yearn (4)
2 Felled (4)
3 Bank account fraud; rumour-mongering (4-6)
4 Almost (6)
6 Viking warship (8)
7 Carried in womb (8)
9 French sculptor (5)
12 Lest (4,2,4)
14 Artillery weapon (8)
15 Ten march (anag.) (8)
18 Go (5)
20 Crumbly (pastry); starchy (potatoes) (6)
22 Hebridean island (4)
23 Land forces (4)

Across

1 *Complain; goldfish* (4)
4 *Way in* (5)
8 Regain (8)
9 Per head (4)
10 Brag (4)
11 Reckon (8)
12 Harsh (6)
14 Make certain (6)
16 Plentiful (8)
19 Task; tax (4)
20 Trip (4)
21 Shame (8)
22 Avoid (5)
23 Minute, diminutive (4)

Down

2 Missile, bolt (5)
3 Give (7)
4 Upright (5)
5 Vacuum flask (7)
6 Sailing vessel (5)
7 Polecat (6)
13 Disregarded (7)
14 Obsolete (7)
15 Plump (6)
17 Wide (5)
18 Nimble (5)
19 Fiend (5)

97

Across

1 *Elevated* (4)
4 *Bowl* (3)
6 *Tavern* (3)
9 *Employment; utilise* (3)
10 Astonish (5)
11 Concerning; roughly (5)
12 Left (9)
15 Raw, unskilled (13)
19 Worker (9)
21 Short (5)
22 Normal (5)
24 Donkey (3)
25 Female sheep (3)
26 Epoch (3)
27 Hut (4)

Down

2 Repeat (7)
3 Amass (5)
4 Vegetable (3)
5 Foot-pedal (7)
6 Snow hut (5)
7 Tidy (4)
8 Madman (7)
13 Care for (5)
14 Hostile (7)
16 Copious (7)
17 Weather (7)
18 Passage (5)
20 Map book (5)
21 Pedestal (4)
23 Vase (3)

98

Across

1 *Standard* (3)
3 *Peck* (4)
5 *Mountain lake* (4)
8 Eastern European (8)
10 Rebuff (4)
11 Primate (3)
13 Register (5)
14 African country (9)
16 Terminus (3)
17 Deed (3)
19 If all goes well (9)
21 Mediterranean fruit (5)
22 Insect (3)
24 Part of eye (4)
25 Ominous (8)
26 — *Karenina*, Tolstoy novel (4)
27 Consequently (4)
28 Fizzy drink (3)

Down

1 Excuse (4)
2 Speed (4)
3 Bird (10)
4 Ancient Greek city (6)
6 Peculiar (8)
7 Peerage (8)
9 Engender (5)
12 Tough situation (3,2,5)
14 Hard wheat grains (8)
15 Supplement (8)
18 Replica (5)
20 Outcast (6)
22 Situated on (4)
23 Stumble (4)

The Telegraph

99

Across

1 *Petit —, fancy biscuit* (4)
3 *Thomas Hardy girl* (4)
9 *Tailback* (5)
10 Ad-lib (9)
11 Go in (5)
12 Optical instrument (9)
15 Queasiness (6)
17 Safe (6)
19 Theatre (9)
21 Firearm (5)
23 Trustworthy (9)
24 Freight (5)
25 Uncommon (4)
26 Parched (4)

Down

1 Frivolous (8)
2 Boxer's blow (8)
4 Use (6)
5 Compress (7)
6 Departed (4)
7 Expensive (4)
8 Flip (4)
13 Salad vegetable (8)
14 Clergyman (8)
16 Ruler (7)
18 Cosset (6)
20 Loathe (4)
21 Wealthy (4)
22 Rage (4)

The Telegraph

100

Across

1 *Female relative* (4)
3 *Channel-hop* (4)
6 *Personal* (3)
9 Difficult saying? (6-7)
10 Fox (8)
12 Observe (4)
13 Pester (3)
15 Threaten (6)
18 Coarsely (6)
19 Add (up) (3)
21 Matured (4)
22 Under 768 mph (8)
25 Held without contact (13)
26 Objective (3)
27 Lacy curtains (4)
28 Indian dish (4)

Down

1 Definitive (13)
2 Tonne (anag.) ; music for a group (5)
4 Improvement (6)
5 Be unsuccessful (4)
6 Result (7)
7 Kindergarten (7,6)
8 Increase (7)
11 Pitch (3)
14 Armed vessel (7)
16 Impaled (7)
17 Operating system (3)
20 Uproar (6)
23 Welsh town (5)
24 Augury (4)

101

Across

1 *Italian wine* (4)
3 *New Zealander* (4)
6 *Equipment* (3)
9 Opening move (7-6)
10 A utensil (anag) (8)
12 Spirit (4)
13 Breakfast food (3)
15 Regard highly (6)
18 Loads (6)
19 Block (river) (3)
21 Snare (4)
22 Fastens (8)
25 Deplorable (13)
26 Fib (3)
27 Saved (4)
28 Authentic (4)

Down

1 Of design (13)
2 Conditions (5)
4 Light (6)
5 Prayer leader (4)
6 Bird of prey (7)
7 Cat; butterfly (13)
8 Domed (7)
11 Self-importance (3)
14 Of no faith (7)
16 Flatten (7)
17 Plan (3)
20 Invented (4,2)
23 Wire (5)
24 Look for (4)

The Telegraph

102

Across

1 *Pine* (5)
4 *Stomach* (3)
6 *Skill* (3)
8 Dally (13)
9 Quits (5)
11 Conduit (4)
13 Cog (5)
14 Song (5)
15 Because (5)
16 Clasp (4)
18 Pointed (5)
21 Immediate (13)
23 Cease (3)
24 Mat (3)
25 Residence (5)

Down

1 Barked (6)
2 Declare (4)
3 Audacity (5)
4 Chatter (3)
5 Hungry (7)
6 Slaughterhouse (8)
7 Channel (6)
10 Surplus (5)
12 Bewildered (8)
14 Hopelessness (7)
15 Writer (6)
17 Chase (6)
19 Animal (5)
20 Alone (4)
22 Label (3)

103

Across

1 *Jetty* (4)
3 *Guides* (6)
8 Unfamiliar (7)
9 Estimate (5)
10 Detest (5)
11 Frighten (7)
12 Euphoric (6)
14 Niche (6)
18 Imprecise (7)
20 Student (5)
22 Reluctant (5)
23 Filch (7)
24 Stopped (6)
25 Perimeter (4)

Down

1 Aisle (7)
2 Soil (5)
3 Detective (6)
4 Enthusiastic (5)
5 Monotonous (7)
6 Fallacious (6)
7 Exceedingly (4)
13 Mediocre (7)
15 Perish (6)
16 Quiet (7)
17 Brainless (6)
18 Lazy (4)
19 Remains (5)
21 Arrogant (5)

104

Across

1 *Liz —, model/actress* (6)
4 *Spoke emphasising 'r'* (6)
7 Local name for Cambodia (9)
9 Sell (4)
10 Box-office failure (4)
11 Yields (5)
13 Walk slowly (6)
14 Refuse to accept (6)
15 Old Persian ruler (6)
17 Fruit (6)
19 Show (5)
20 Gentle accent (4)
22 Small particle (4)
23 Listlessness (9)
24 Abdicate (6)
25 My dear (anag.) (6)

Down

1 Reduced by 50% (6)
2 Heavy metal (4)
3 Hurray (6)
4 Squabble (6)
5 Underwater rock (4)
6 Tyrant (6)
7 Unteachable bigot (4-2-3)
8 Take turns (9)
11 Not cloudy (5)
12 Musical transition (5)
15 Precious metal (6)
16 Human being (6)
17 Cited (6)
18 Hostility (6)
21 Cab (4)
22 Tool (4)

The Telegraph

105

Across

1 *Monarch's period* (5)
4 *Means of payment* (6)
9 Cattle thief (7)
10 Deal with superficially (5)
11 Army vehicle (4)
12 Very cold compartment (7)
13 Write hurriedly (3)
14 S. American country (4)
16 Bad-mannered (4)
18 Waterless (3)
20 Criminal action (7)
21 Persian ruler (4)
24 Queen's dog? (5)
25 Jumble of letters (7)
26 Beefeaters? (6)
27 Attire (5)

Down

1 Something unusual (6)
2 Norwegian author (5)
3 African river (4)
5 Inn (8)
6 Questioned (7)
7 Dab (6)
8 Hard work (5)
13 Non-adult (8)
15 Barrier to trade (7)
17 Involving snags (6)
18 & 19 Welsh poet (5,6)
22 Great crowd (5)
23 Hospital room (4)

106

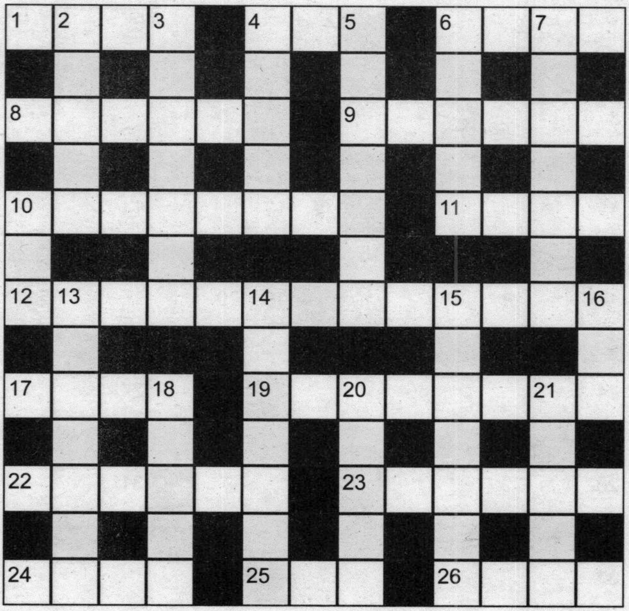

Across

1 *Planet* (4)
4 *Hat* (3)
6 *Small horse* (4)
8 *Dairy product* (6)
9 Tiny (6)
10 Gap in wood (8)
11 Part of *26 Across* (4)
12 Projectile (6,7)
17 Wound mark (4)
19 Coin slot (anag.) (8)
22 Dairy product (6)
23 Inside (6)
24 Part of *26 Across* (4)
25 Mire (3)
26 White liquid (4)

Down

2 Grey (5)
3 Sweet-smelling (7)
4 Set of beliefs (5)
5 Old Italian city (7)
6 Alarm (5)
7 Unaffected (7)
10 Cask (3)
13 Uncultured (7)
14 Dignity (7)
15 Holy place (7)
16 Consume (3)
18 Irritable (5)
20 Mooed (5)
21 Eddy (5)

107

Across

1 *Aromatic herb* (5)
4 *Pilgrimage site* (7)
8 Work unit (3)
9 Base fellow (3)
10 Brief performance (5)
11 The real thing (5)
12 Metal band (7)
15 Mexican money (4)
17 Afternoon break (6)
19 Person renting (6)
22 Counterfeit (4)
24 Worzel Gummidge actor (7)
26 Bread maker (5)
28 Tasty fish (5)
30 Heavy weight (3)
31 Former boxer (3)
32 Cattle farmer (7)
33 Metalworker (5)

Down

1 Vacuum flask (7)
2 Of Hindu philosophy (5)
3 Put into code (7)
4 Words of a song (6)
5 Sore spot (5)
6 Not very bright (3)
7 Reconnoitre (5)
13 Tiny amount (4)
14 Meadow (3)
16 Comfort (4)
18 Sense organ (3)
20 Encloses with an earth wall (7)
21 Take the shine off (7)
23 Boss around (6)
24 Safe; saint (5)
25 Bad speller! (5)
27 Drab colour (5)
29 Possess (3)

The Telegraph

108

Across

1 *Purchase* (3)
3 *Cobbler's tool* (3)
5 *Method; resources* (5)
8 Musical drama (5)
9 Genuine (7)
10 Conceal (4)
11 Trader (8)
13 Kidnap (6)
14 Ebb (6)
17 Obtained (8)
19 Second-hand (4)
22 Non-professional (7)
23 Motif (5)
24 Larceny (5)
25 Deviate (3)
26 Nothing (3)

Down

1 Stall (5)
2 Conceded (7)
3 Sad to say (4)
4 Diminish (6)
5 Handcuffs (8)
6 Ring; stadium (5)
7 Ghost (7)
12 Mishap (8)
13 Resolute (7)
15 Oriental (7)
16 Be disloyal; reveal (6)
18 Tremble (5)
20 Reside (5)
21 Put away (4)

The Telegraph

109

Across

1 *Wagon* (4)
3 *Whiten* (6)
9 Wise (7)
10 Grating (5)
11 Flightless bird (3)
12 Allegedly (9)
13 The cloth (6)
14 Female warrior; river (6)
16 Crucial (9)
19 Chopper (3)
21 Around (5)
22 Insensitive (7)
23 Exertion (6)
24 Children's alphabet game (1,3)

Down

1 Class (5)
2 Ecstasy (7)
4 Rightfully (12)
5 Water nymph (5)
6 Peaceful; golden (7)
7 Freezer (12)
8 Pace (4)
13 Weather (7)
15 Ardent (7)
17 Evidence (5)
18 Roguish (4)
20 Composition (5)

Across

1 *Tailback* (5)
4 *Sleep rough* (4)
8 Deed (3)
9 Rash (9)
10 Bunker; carriage (4)
11 Border (8)
12 Trophy; kitty (3)
13 Paltry (6)
14 Digit (6)
16 Offer (3)
17 Hand over (8)
18 Hitch (4)
20 Auk (9)
21 Bird of prey (3)
22 Repair (4)
23 Penny-pincher (5)

Down

1 Amount (7)
2 Lavish display (12)
3 Way out (4)
4 Leave (6)
5 Magnificent (8)
6 Insincere (12)
7 Expensive (4)
11 Enemy (3)
12 Jam; safeguard (8)
14 Coniferous tree (3)
15 Done frequently (7)
16 After (6)
17 Word, expression (4)
19 Dejected (4)

The Telegraph

111

Across

1 *Gangster's girlfriend* (4)
4 *English port* (5)
8 Dull, antiquated figure (3,5)
9 Dupe (4)
10 Despot (4)
11 Cornish town (8)
12 Australian city (6)
14 Notebook (6)
16 Interrogate (8)
19 Resist (4)
20 Norse god (4)
21 Uselessness (8)
22 Stationery item (5)
23 Smell (4)

Down

2 Present (5)
3 Type of bowling (3,4)
4 Senior member (5)
5 Tramp (7)
6 E.g. saint's bone (5)
7 Liquid part of blood (6)
13 Profligate (7)
14 Caretaker (7)
15 Rouse (6)
17 Escort (5)
18 Deduce (5)
19 Swell (5)

112

Across

1 *Hardwood tree* (3)
3 *Pain* (4)
5 *Viva voce* (4)
8 French region (8)
10 Banner (4)
11 Pose (3)
13 Be of use to (5)
14 Crooked (9)
16 Poem (3)
17 Fate (3)
19 Big guns (9)
21 Praise (5)
22 Implore (3)
24 Labour (4)
25 US game (8)
26 Masticate (4)
27 Price (4)
28 Finish (3)

Down

1 Clumsy me! (4)
2 Nautical speed (4)
3 Improve (10)
4 Barrack (6)
6 Trustworthy (8)
7 Lawfulness (8)
9 Stiff (5)
12 Crenellation (10)
14 Of the home (8)
15 Tranquilliser (8)
18 Type of window (5)
20 Love apple (6)
22 Foundation (4)
23 Pleased (4)

The Telegraph

113

Across

1 *Capital of Ecuador* (5)
4 *Clunk* (4)
8 *Reverence* (3)
9 Associate (9)
10 Mature (4)
11 Incompetent, feeble (8)
12 Tart (3)
13 Lasso (6)
14 Water gate (6)
16 Aviate (3)
17 Exaggerate (8)
18 Fit, fever (4)
20 Bribes (9)
21 Eggs (3)
22 Tang, relish (4)
23 Concede (5)

Down

1 Argue (7)
2 Rawness (12)
3 Spoken (4)
4 Caramel (6)
5 Improbable (8)
6 Oasis (8,4)
7 Planes (4)
11 Suit (3)
12 Tangible (8)
14 Cunning (3)
15 Green; gem (7)
16 Tap (6)
17 People not posh (4)
19 Spot (4)

114

Across

7 *Fire* (4)
8 *Beam* (3)
9 *Haze* (4)
10 Fluffy decorative ball (6)
11 Test run (3-3)
12 Sick (3)
13 Joints (6)
14 Respect (6)
16 Prickly desert plant (6)
19 Shrewd (6)
21 Bundle (3)
22 Cereal (6)
24 Bereft (6)
25 Reminder (4)
26 Sheep (3)
27 Cheeky child (4)

Down

1 Pool (6)
2 Military chaplain (3,5)
3 One Musketeer (6)
4 Fragrant evergreen (6)
5 Comply with (4)
6 Surgical stitching (6)
15 Smarten up (8)
17 Lucky charm (6)
18 Pivot (6)
19 Confused (6)
20 Awkward (6)
23 Deposit in chimney (4)

115

Across

1 *Recognise* (4)
4 *Wreck* (4)
8 *Difficult* (4)
9 Detestable (9)
11 Fair (6)
13 Split (7)
15 Starry (6)
16 Cause (6)
18 Foray (6)
20 Swindle (6)
22 Cross (7)
23 Inaudible (6)
25 Fleeting (9)
26 Declaim (4)
27 Work (4)
28 Impulsive (4)

Down

2 Midday (4)
3 Shrivel (6)
4 Inn (6)
5 Flexible (6)
6 Decorated (9)
7 Advantage (4)
10 Aged (7)
12 Girl (4)
13 Extraordinary (9)
14 Courageous (7)
17 Necessity (4)
19 Capture (6)
20 Establishes (6)
21 Stranger (6)
23 Painful (4)
24 Insects (4)

116

Across

1 *Line of people* (5)
4 *Luxurious hotel* (4)
8 Unconventional (7)
9 Smell (5)
10 Heron (5)
11 Dairy product (7)
13 Corrects (6)
15 Motorist (6)
17 Passage from work (7)
20 Sweetheart (5)
22 Address to boy (5)
23 Designed (7)
24 Retain (4)
25 Rubbish (5)

Down

1 Cite (5)
2 Bubbly (12)
3 Thrown out (7)
4 Irritable (5)
5 Skimpy undergarment (5)
6 Way of life (5,7)
7 Author (6)
12 Strange (3)
13 Discrimination e.g. against old people (6)
14 Concession (3)
16 Latrine (anag.) (7)
18 'Moon' and 'June' do (5)
19 Refill of drink (3-2)
21 Raised strip (5)

The Telegraph

117

Across

1 *Grumbler* (6)
4 *Resale (anag.)* (6)
7 Whining (9)
9 Burden (4)
10 Shift (4)
11 Change (5)
13 Blood vessel (6)
14 Small bag (6)
15 Lowest point (6)
17 Not natural (6)
19 Town near Manchester (5)
20 Top covering (4)
22 Religious group (4)
23 Late drinks (9)
24 Stylish (6)
25 Building extension (6)

Down

1 Tropical shrub (6)
2 Common sense (4)
3 Very infrequently (6)
4 Flowering plants (6)
5 Sulphate; maul (anag.) (4)
6 Turn down (6)
7 Citation (9)
8 Greek tragedian (9)
11 Projectile from bow (5)
12 Artificial material (5)
15 Muslim garments (6)
16 Powerful (6)
17 Surface over shop window (6)
18 Senility (6)
21 Effervescence (4)
22 Rotate quickly (4)

118

Across

1 *Period of rule* (5)
5 *Handsome men* (5)
8 Basket material (5)
9 Royal house (5)
10 Urgent messages (9)
11 Urge (on) (3)
12 Changing (a decision) (11)
15 Very energetic person (5,6)
19 Type of wine (3)
20 Drinker's paunch (4,5)
22 Area near to bull's-eye (5)
23 Utter contempt (5)
24 Drive from home (5)
25 Village space (5)

Down

1 Cut down expenditure (8)
2 Plant dye (6)
3 Towards the Arctic (8)
4 Herbaceous flower (6)
5 Card game (4)
6 Opposite of acid (6)
7 Winter festival (informal) (4)
13 Getting prepared (8)
14 American football (8)
16 Breakfast dish (6)
17 Cowardly (6)
18 Fruit (6)
20 Oxbridge sportsman (4)
21 Small statue (4)

The Telegraph

119

Across

1 *Tent site* (4)
3 *– Boleyn* (4)
9 *Science (facetious)* (5)
10 Active at night (9)
11 Internal (5)
12 Medication (9)
15 A perch (anag.) (6)
17 Aft (6)
19 Harassing (9)
21 Allocation (5)
23 Hoaxer (3-6)
24 Bring on oneself (5)
25 Jerk (4)
26 First man (4)

Down

1 Empty tomb (8)
2 Sea fish (8)
4 Western French port (6)
5 Early stone implements (7)
6 Amalgamate (4)
7 Cloth-stainer (4)
8 Bankrupt (4)
13 Leo cried (anag.) (8)
14 Unit of wavelength measurement (8)
16 Mounted soldiers (7)
18 Gas (6)
20 Trip (4)
21 Panel game (4)
22 In days past (4)

![The Telegraph]

120

Across

1 *Column* (6)
4 *Twisting force* (6)
7 Vain; narcissistic (9)
9 Break (4)
10 Jump (4)
11 Spirit measure (5)
13 Threaten (6)
14 Assert (6)
15 Consume (6)
17 Haphazard (6)
19 Crow-like bird (5)
20 Biblical priest (4)
22 Spurn, ignore (4)
23 Well-organised (9)
24 Annual (6)
25 Number; statue (6)

Down

1 Play — (pretend to be dead) (6)
2 Noose (4)
3 Cooking directions (6)
4 Minutiae (6)
5 Stagger (4)
6 Pass (time) (6)
7 Flesh-eating animal (9)
8 Protégé (9)
11 Happen (5)
12 Spotless; launder (5)
15 Gloomy (6)
16 Authenticate (6)
17 Help (6)
18 Portable (6)
21 At a distance (4)
22 Difficulty; catch (4)

121

Across

1 *Violin* (6)
5 *Hades river* (4)
8 Minus (4)
9 Caribou (8)
10 Flatfish (6)
11 Strip (6)
12 Vanished (11)
15 Brusque (6)
17 Leave (6)
19 Mishap (8)
20 Unsightly (4)
21 Gala (4)
22 Dismal (6)

Down

2 Perfect (5)
3 Sack (7)
4 Weird (5)
5 Carrying chair (5)
6 Ceded (7)
7 Sieve; enigma (6)
12 Fiasco (7)
13 Golf-club (6)
14 Ecstasy (7)
16 Combine (5)
17 Archaic; took out (5)
18 Monarch (5)

The Telegraph

122

Across

1 *To weary* (4)
3 *Joint* (4)
6 *Be in debt* (3)
9 TV accessory (6,7)
10 Undertake (8)
12 Chant (4)
13 Thighs, when seated (3)
15 Recruit (6)
18 Trendy (4,2)
19 Success (3)
21 Instant (4)
22 Friar (8)
25 Distasteful (13)
26 Church bench (3)
27 Prevalent (4)
28 Let it stand (editing mark) (4)

Down

1 Chinese dish (5-4,4)
2 Shakespearean character (5)
4 US coin (6)
5 Sea-eagle (4)
6 Monstrous (7)
7 Illumination (13)
8 Chic (7)
11 Uncooked (3)
14 Appetising, tangy (7)
16 Tetanus (7)
17 Involuntary response (3)
20 Customs duty (6)
23 Dress (5)
24 Blemish (4)

The Telegraph

123

Across

1 *Croaky* (6)
5 *Encounter* (4)
8 Halt (4)
9 Hellish (8)
10 Charge (6)
11 Custom (6)
12 Showiness (11)
15 Merchant (6)
17 Magnificent (6)
19 Clergyman (8)
20 US state (4)
21 Touch (4)
22 Fantastic (6)

Down

2 Frequently (5)
3 Model (7)
4 Have life (5)
5 Goodness (5)
6 Give out (7)
7 Brawl (6)
12 Fecund (7)
13 Scold (6)
14 Planet (7)
16 Training (5)
17 Scrap (5)
18 Kingdom (5)

124

Across

1 *Water defences* (5)
5 *Courage* (5)
8 Ciao (5)
9 Head monk (5)
10 Unknowing (9)
11 Highs (3)
12 Boxing category (11)
15 Cruel employer (5-6)
19 Vase (3)
20 Roman revolutionary (9)
22 Accounts check (5)
23 Fork (5)
24 Kicks (5)
25 Soil (5)

Down

1 Evaluates (8)
2 Lie in wait; trap (6)
3 Soak (8)
4 Respiratory tract (6)
5 Damage (4)
6 Suffering (6)
7 Sharp taste (4)
13 Picture (8)
14 First-rate (3-5)
16 Slowly (music) (6)
17 Estimate (6)
18 Steering mechanism (6)
20 Cut; ignore (4)
21 Bugs (wire) (4)

125

Across

1 *Austere* (5)
4 *Sheen* (6)
9 Lunar trajectory (5)
10 Wideness (7)
11 Take away (7)
12 Root vegetable (5)
14 Beam (3)
15 Loose, careless (3)
16 Sardonic (3)
18 Part of circle (3)
21 Purchaser (5)
22 Anguish (7)
23 Loud applause (7)
25 Supply (food) (5)
26 Agent (6)
27 Fashion (5)

Down

1 Cheap, inferior (6)
2 Capricious (9)
3 Knapsack (6)
5 Nervous (6)
6 A slight amount (3)
7 Repeats (6)
8 Blocking (11)
13 Seriously (9)
17 Soak up (6)
18 Get there (6)
19 Finds; signs (6)
20 Go hungry (6)
24 Trouble (3)

126

Across

1 *Battle* (3)
3 *Bath* (3)
5 *Principal* (4)
7 Bashful (5)
8 Quit (6)
10 Plunge (4)
11 Anticlimax (8)
13 United (6)
14 Culminate (6)
17 Outrage (8)
19 Copies (4)
21 Vary (6)
22 Perfume (5)
23 Inferno (4)
24 Certainly (3)
25 Dine (3)

Down

1 Departure (10)
2 Ejection (7)
3 Neat (4)
4 Scrounge (6)
5 Frenzy (8)
6 Bovver (5)
9 Devotee (10)
12 Humane (8)
15 Enhance (7)
16 Robust (6)
18 Elevate (5)
20 Girl (4)

127

Across

1 *Cashier* (6)
4 *Floor* (6)
9 Let in (5)
10 Flexible (7)
11 Edge (3)
12 Attempt (5)
13 Foretell (7)
15 Turned so icy (anag.) (11)
19 Drug seller (7)
20 Irish-born painter (5)
21 Avail oneself of (3)
22 More irate (7)
24 Room in the roof (5)
25 Guard (6)
26 Pursues (6)

Down

1 Followed (6)
2 Rock of calcium carbonate (9)
3 Way in (5)
5 Sellers (7)
6 Informer (3)
7 Light sailing-vessels (6)
8 Degree of hotness (11)
14 Shows (9)
16 More loud (7)
17 Fights (6)
18 Criticises (6)
20 Coast (5)
23 Shooter (3)

The Telegraph

128

Across

1 *Manufactured* (4)
3 *Regatta town* (6)
9 Not the same (7)
10 Manages (5)
11 Termination (3)
12 Dutch capital (9)
13 Brigand (6)
14 Commandeer (6)
16 Emotional purge (9)
19 Favourite (3)
21 City in Florida (5)
22 Carry out (7)
23 Adage (6)
24 Quarrel (4)

Down

1 Purplish colour (5)
2 German city (7)
4 OT book (12)
5 Organic compound (5)
6 Muslim veil (7)
7 Compassionate (12)
8 Unfortunately (4)
13 Turns into (7)
15 Small container (7)
17 Bootlicker (5)
18 1956 trouble spot (4)
20 Material; river (5)

129

Across

1 *Male sheep* (6)
4 *Pronged implement* (4)
9 *Nancy —, one-time MP* (5)
10 Scottish insurgent (7)
11 Related (7)
12 Suppress (5)
13 Canine mammal (6)
15 Lea (6)
18 Dark time (5)
20 Pithy (7)
23 Let off (7)
24 & 17 Down Whisker-remover (5,5)
25 Pig's noise (4)
26 Compass directions (6)

Down

1 Hard hit (5)
2 Ill-fated liner (7)
3 Mistake (5)
5 Slanting (7)
6 Jack (card) (5)
7 Root vegetable (5)
8 Colour of cowardice (6)
13 Milky dessert (6)
14 Skilled worker (7)
16 Inhabitant (7)
17 *See 24 Across*
19 Lizard (5)
21 Transported goods (5)
22 Army unit (5)

The Telegraph

130

Across

1 *Chopper* (3)
3 *Ocean* (3)
5 *Hollow* (4)
7 Agree (5)
8 Dwell (6)
10 Wander (4)
11 Percussion instrument (4,4)
13 Peckish (6)
14 Balkan country (6)
17 Tragedy (8)
19 Fortune (4)
21 Meagre (6)
22 Gatehouse (5)
23 Hero (4)
24 Not cooked (3)
25 Deserter (3)

Down

1 Tremor following earthquake (10)
2 Animate (7)
3 Type of bean (4)
4 Overseas (6)
5 Catastrophe (8)
6 Drain (anag.) (5)
9 Mound (10)
12 Lawbreaker (8)
15 Mistake (7)
16 Persistent person (6)
18 Intertwined (5)
20 Strong current of air (4)

The Telegraph

131

Across

1 *Angry* (5)
4 *Spun, making a sound* (7)
8 *Animal smell* (5)
9 *Victorian illustrator* (7)
10 Weapons store (7)
11 Drinking spree (5)
12 Formal or elegant (6)
14 Royal comedian (6)
18 Place for discussion (5)
20 Very old (7)
22 A daydream (7)
23 Small pancake (5)
24 The close of a day (7)
25 Not illegal (5)

Down

1 Pudding accompaniment (7)
2 Supervise (7)
3 Glossy material (5)
4 Turkey's dangly bit (6)
5 Unworthy (7)
6 Period of rule (5)
7 Dig into (5)
13 Japanese warrior (7)
15 Exchanging (7)
16 A written acknowledgement (7)
17 Unpleasant person (3,3)
18 Smith's workshop (5)
19 Stage show (5)
21 Group in plot (5)

132

Across

7 *Knocked* (6)
8 *Reply* (6)
10 To haggle (7)
11 Dismantle (5)
13 Level (4)
15 Chasm (5)
17 Rot (5)
19 Converse (4)
23 Striped animal (5)
25 Bullfighter (7)
26 Withstand (6)
27 Young swan (6)

Down

1 Durable; horse shed (6)
2 Scanty (6)
3 Postpone (5)
4 Distress (7)
5 Pitcher (4)
6 Boast; card game (4)
9 Cold-shoulder (4)
12 Perfect (5)
14 Worth (5)
16 By reason (of) (7)
18 Zenith (4)
20 Passionate (6)
21 A martial art (6)
22 Corset (5)
23 Nothing (4)
24 Smite; a party (4)

The Telegraph

133

Across

1 *Easter treats!* (4)
3 *Steed* (5)
7 *Magnitude* (4)
8 Dreadful (10)
9 Atmosphere (4)
12 Cul-de-sacs (5,6)
13 Pulled along (5)
15 Scrounge (5)
19 A booking (11)
21 Swelling (4)
23 Withdrawal (10)
24 Indian dress (4)
25 Vacant (5)
26 Informed (4)

Down

1 Show (of art) (10)
2 Weird (7)
3 Airport shed (6)
4 Dig with snout (6)
5 Try (5)
6 Russian ruler (alt. spelling) (4)
10 Exploited (4)
11 Took turns (10)
14 Part of hospital (4)
16 Effort; go (7)
17 Repressed (4-2)
18 Too (6)
20 Spooky (5)
22 Opaque gem (4)

134

Across

1 *Praise or glorify* (4)
4 *Female horse* (4)
8 Instrument (4)
9 Pistol (9)
11 Polecat; search (6)
13 Escort (4,3)
15 Window (6)
16 Probable (6)
18 Over-refined, pretentious (6)
20 Writer (6)
22 Difficult to chew (7)
23 Tray (6)
25 Wagner opera (9)
26 Apartment (4)
27 Jaunty (4)
28 Young cow (4)

Down

2 Summit (4)
3 English county (6)
4 Long trough (6)
5 Apologetic (6)
6 Crisp biscuit (9)
7 Achievement (4)
10 Entourage (7)
12 Lazy (4)
13 Naval battle (9)
14 Small falcon (7)
17 Enclosure (4)
19 Continent (6)
20 Away (6)
21 Disastrous (6)
23 Velvety (4)
24 Factory (4)

135

Across

1 *Posted* (4)
4 *Notch; steal* (4)
8 *Sad to say* (4)
9 Noel (9)
11 Vie; compete (6)
13 Moving mass of ice (7)
15 Moon goddess (6)
16 Preferably (6)
18 Dome (6)
20 Items of business (6)
22 Floating ice mass (7)
23 Jesus (6)
25 Very funny (9)
26 Skating ice (4)
27 Guide; precede (4)
28 Level (4)

Down

2 Reverberate (4)
3 Party dessert (6)
4 See (6)
5 Beer after spirits e.g. (6)
6 Sledging (9)
7 Small island (4)
10 Unfamiliar (7)
12 Heroic (4)
13 Baptism sponsor (9)
14 Get rid of (7)
17 Wander (4)
19 Busy (6)
20 On ship (6)
21 Winter stoat (6)
23 Greetings __ (4)
24 Christmas season (4)

The Telegraph

136

Across

1 *Hairpiece* (6)
4 *As soon as* (4)
9 *Consider* (5)
10 Contrast (7)
11 Bane (7)
12 Relative (5)
13 Primes (anag.) (6)
15 Promise (6)
18 Card game (5)
20 Earphones (7)
23 Reasons (7)
24 Refrain from (5)
25 Type of window (4)
26 Sex (6)

Down

1 Municipalities (5)
2 Regular (7)
3 An anaesthetic (5)
5 Token (7)
6 Duck (5)
7 Hurts (5)
8 Strict (6)
13 Waste matter (6)
14 Stretches (7)
16 Dissension (7)
17 Be quiet (5)
19 Golf clubs (5)
21 Mindful (5)
22 Royal dynasty (5)

The Telegraph

137

Across

1 *Cursed* (5)
4 *Botch* (4)
7 *Untruths* (4)
8 Rational (8)
9 Horrific (9)
10 Modern (3)
12 Gambol (6)
14 Thin (6)
16 Ancient (3)
18 Diminutive (9)
21 Heaven (8)
22 Sadly (4)
23 Enthusiastic (4)
24 Supple (5)

Down

1 Captain (7)
2 Hindrance (8)
3 Outdo (5)
4 Additional (4)
5 Barrier (5)
6 Gratitude (6)
11 Sidetrack (8)
13 Emergency (6)
15 Recount (7)
17 Depart (5)
19 Perfect (5)
20 Sunrise (4)

The Telegraph

138

Across

1 *Blackthorn fruit* (4)
3 *Cigarette end* (4)
9 *Seafront* (5)
10 Built-up district (5,4)
11 Drive back (5)
12 Rabble (3,6)
15 OK (6)
17 Pace (6)
19 National Gallery's Sainsbury Wing? (9)
21 Aviator (5)
23 Bankrupt (9)
24 Expressing emotion (5)
25 Not bad (2-2)
26 Heal (4)

Down

1 From below the Mason-Dixon Line (8)
2 Home of the Boat Race crews (8)
4 Mutinous (6)
5 Supporter of the Russian Empire (7)
6 Broth (4)
7 Rind (4)
8 Gen (4)
13 Separate (8)
14 Glum (8)
16 Strategy (7)
18 Pub snack (6)
20 Threatening (4)
21 Skin (4)
22 Escapade (4)

139

Across

1 *Age of majority* (8)
7 *Trimming tool* (5)
8 Feeling (9)
9 Annoy (3)
10 Injure (4)
11 Small wolf (6)
13 Canadian city (6)
14 Flotsam and – (6)
17 Get (6)
18 Rubbish tip (4)
20 Male swan (3)
22 Avidity (9)
23 Defeated competitor (5)
24 Bully (8)

Down

1 Derby racecourse (5)
2 Non-Jew (7)
3 Melting process (4)
4 US inventor (6)
5 Tropical plant (5)
6 Devon fishing town (7)
7 Relished (7)
12 Wing component (7)
13 At speed (7)
15 Compress (7)
16 Vocalist (6)
17 Very fat (5)
19 Postulate (5)
21 Increase (4)

140

Across

1 *Volcanic vents* (8)
7 *Sobs* (5)
8 Turf accountant (9)
9 Possess (3)
10 Go first (4)
11 Wine jug (6)
13 Temporary house (6)
14 Memorial tablet (6)
17 City in *5 Down* (6)
18 Record (4)
20 Drink; meal (3)
22 Abusive language (9)
23 Devoured (5)
24 Unseemly (8)

Down

1 Clique (5)
2 Set apart (7)
3 Identification (4)
4 Country bumpkins (6)
5 English county (5)
6 Mindless (7)
7 Move like worm (7)
12 Athletics missile (7)
13 Knot-shaped cracker (7)
15 Anti-malarial drug (7)
16 Blessed abode (6)
17 Our planet (5)
19 Storage box (5)
21 Unit of land area (4)

141

Across

1 *Front-runner* (6)
4 *Watering plants* (6)
7 Invertebrates (8)
9 John —, English dramatist (7)
12 Base of alcohol (5)
13 Force (5)
15 Frill of lace (5)
16 Pale (5)
17 Like yellow part of egg (5)
18 Self-evident truth (5)
19 Cookhouse (7)
23 Coasting (anag.) (8)
24 Heraldic dragon (6)
25 Unaccented (6)

Down

1 Feller (10)
2 A greeting (3,3,4)
3 Sameness (8)
4 Catcall (4)
5 Starchy cereal (4)
6 Gaseous element (4)
8 Creating a collection (9)
10 Give a new name to (10)
11 Frugal (10)
14 Lazy person (8)
20 Dubious (4)
21 Clerical vestment; to deal (with) (4)
22 Merit (4)

142

Across

1 *Unpleasantly wet* (4)
3 *Marine mammal* (5)
7 Pile of hay (4)
8 Head of university (10)
9 Pig sound (4)
12 US bravery award (6,5)
13 African antelope (5)
15 Character (5)
19 Print for checking (6,5)
21 Part of old phone (4)
23 Thin pasta (10)
24 Spanish surrealist painter (4)
25 Work for nine players (5)
26 Large volume (4)

Down

1 Extracted from code (10)
2 Ring leader (7)
3 Cleared garden (6)
4 Resting unconscious (6)
5 Blunder (5)
6 Study systematically (4)
10 Strong desire (4)
11 Emergency resuscitation (4,2,4)
14 Seaweed (4)
16 Heavy stream (7)
17 Pre-decimal coin (6)
18 Pre-computer office worker (6)
20 — Stardust, singer (5)
22 Muslim cleric (4)

143

Across

1 *Keen* (5)
4 *Apparel* (7)
8 Raised (7)
9 Hackneyed (5)
10 Upright (5)
11 Serious (7)
13 Bird; frolic (4)
15 Glimpsed (6)
17 Infuse (6)
20 Region (4)
22 Hauled (7)
24 Stone-worker (5)
26 Stadium (5)
27 Keep; notice (7)
28 College graduate (7)
29 Perfume (5)

Down

1 Attain (7)
2 Combine (5)
3 Call; permit (7)
4 Helm (6)
5 Bury (5)
6 Exalted (7)
7 Larceny (5)
12 Similar (4)
14 Cutting tool (4)
16 Tableland (7)
18 Goddess of revenge (7)
19 Merciful (7)
21 Hateful (6)
22 Play (5)
23 Corn; seed (5)
25 Swell (5)

144

Across

1 *Seaman* (6)
4 *Go back* (6)
7 Assign (8)
9 Resolute (7)
12 Discourage (5)
13 Cook; criticise (5)
15 Massive (5)
16 Hunting dog (5)
17 The same again (5)
18 Helicopter propeller (5)
19 Distinctive (7)
23 Precious (8)
24 Pal (6)
25 Thank you; goodbye! (6)

Down

1 Shocking (10)
2 Unable to read or write (10)
3 Happened (8)
4 Regretted (4)
5 Neat and tidy (4)
6 Precipitation (4)
8 Large tropical spider (9)
10 Modifiable (10)
11 Compassion (10)
14 Painstaking (8)
20 Peep; nobleman (4)
21 Centre (4)
22 Greedy (4)

145

Across

4 *Male sheep* (6)
5 *Futile* (4)
7 Capital city (7)
10 Gradient (5)
11 White ant (7)
12 Ardent male lover (5)
14 Roman emperor (7)
15 Clergyman (5)
16 Experience (7)
20 Vast crowd (5)
21 Brighton school (7)
22 Of sound mind (4)
23 Existing in fact (6)

Down

1 Small carnivore (5)
2 Hungarian composer (5)
3 Sailing ship (7)
4 Frail (4)
6 Male relative (6)
8 French painter (7)
9 More stylish (7)
10 Unusual (7)
13 Renowned (6)
14 Escapologist (7)
17 Freshwater fish (5)
18 Smell (5)
19 Be unsuccessful (4)

146

Across

1 *Excavator* (6)
4 *Complete* (5)
8 Overwhelm (5)
9 Result (7)
10 Prompts (7)
11 Show off (4)
12 Purpose (3)
14 At large (4)
15 Golf club (4)
18 Stain (3)
21 Chance (4)
23 Glimpsed (7)
25 Revere (7)
26 Behave (5)
27 Perch (5)
28 Chief (6)

Down

1 Want (6)
2 Rules of language (7)
3 Grew larger (8)
4 Mental faculties (4)
5 Smell (5)
6 Vigour (6)
7 More serious (5)
13 Dire ages (anag.) (8)
16 Garden of fruit trees (7)
17 Blossom (6)
19 African country (5)
20 Newspaper boss (6)
22 Ship's load (5)
24 Conversation (4)

The Telegraph

147

Across

1 *Poor city area* (6)
4 *Small polecat* (6)
7 Outside (8)
9 Cultured; polite (7)
12 Submerge (5)
13 Shine (5)
15 Relative (5)
16 A lament (5)
17 Vaulted (5)
19 Top of cake (5)
20 Keep up (7)
24 Able to feel (8)
25 Resources (6)
26 Free (6)

Down

1 Gluttony (10)
2 Outgoing people (10)
3 Milled around (8)
4 Dismiss (4)
5 Spellbound (4)
6 Rim (4)
8 Monster (4)
10 Controlled test (10)
11 Sore throat (10)
14 Go-between (8)
18 Colliery (4)
21 Pots (4)
22 Pipe (4)
23 Egyptian goddess (4)

The Telegraph

148

Across

1 *Hearsay* (6)
4 *Played* (5)
8 *Split* (5)
9 *Authors* (7)
10 Release (3,4)
11 Betting price (4)
12 Knock (3)
14 Outer shell (4)
15 Uncommon (4)
18 To nickname (3)
21 Every (4)
23 Not swayed (7)
25 Songbird (7)
26 Trunk (5)
27 Toffee, e.g. (5)
28 Clergyman (6)

Down

1 Work over again (6)
2 Armed force (7)
3 Not merited (8)
4 Cotton on (4)
5 Give way (5)
6 Stop (6)
7 Young hooter (5)
13 Impresario (8)
16 Turn back (7)
17 People count (6)
19 Goes against (5)
20 Skilful (6)
22 Scottish river (5)
24 Sodium chloride (4)

149

Across

1 *Genuine* (4)
4 *Evil* (3)
6 *Fear* (3)
8 Conflict (12)
10 Decent (6)
12 Rarely (6)
13 Uniform (5)
14 Scarf (4)
15 Rabbit's tail (4)
17 African capital (5)
19 Dark (6)
21 Greek god (6)
23 Russian novel (4,8)
24 Cambridgeshire city (3)
25 Lout (3)
26 Shout (4)

Down

2 Destructive (7)
3 Tooth covering (6)
4 Canine noise (4)
5 Type of oil (6)
6 Change (5)
7 Guess (10)
9 Bishopric (10)
11 Theatrical show (5)
12 Cuttlefish ink (5)
16 Army officer (7)
17 Bird (6)
18 Copse (6)
20 Irritate (5)
22 Monotonous (4)

Across

1 *Fibbed* (4)
3 *Comforts* (6)
8 Stuffy (7)
9 Ceasefire (5)
10 Elegance (5)
11 Greed (7)
12 Sprightly (6)
14 Property (6)
18 Dream (7)
20 Sovereign (5)
22 Clergyman (5)
23 Mediocre (7)
24 Erase (6)
25 Photo (4)

Down

1 Affair (7)
2 Premature (5)
3 Nonchalant (6)
4 Accessory (5)
5 Habitual (7)
6 Expose (6)
7 Present (4)
13 Handcuff (7)
15 Scream (6)
16 Excess (7)
17 Whirl (6)
18 Quintet (4)
19 Concur (5)
21 Unwilling (5)

151

Across

1 *Car-friendly refreshment stop* (5-2)
5 *Monarch's period* (5)
8 Unsatisfactory repair (5)
9 Fabric (7)
10 Huntsperson's cry (5-2)
11 Native of old Mexico (5)
12 Canadian province (6)
14 In abeyance (2,4)
17 Suggest (5)
19 Instilling wonder (7)
22 Fraudulent (7)
23 Connects (5)
24 Minor prophet (5)
25 French department (7)

Down

1 First appearance (5)
2 Gratify (7)
3 Foe (5)
4 Idea (6)
5 Chorus (7)
6 Lacking skill (5)
7 Given subtle variation (7)
12 Speed up (7)
13 Place of the blessed (7)
15 Of Oxford uni (7)
16 Unit of depth (6)
18 Fruit (5)
20 Relish (5)
21 Follow (5)

152

Across

1 *Epidemic disease* (6)
4 *Circular* (5)
8 Excuse in court (5)
9 Financial statement (7)
10 Lawn sport (7)
11 Reasonable (4)
12 School of Buddhism (3)
14 Small rail station (4)
15 Charitable giving (4)
18 Nevertheless (3)
21 Impetuous (4)
23 OT patriarch (7)
25 Set aside for future use (7)
26 Pirates' treasure? (5)
27 Juice in rubber-making (5)
28 Accent; shoe (6)

Down

1 Fish (6)
2 Grand Canyon state (7)
3 Omnipresence (8)
4 Wealthy (4)
5 Flap in throat (5)
6 One old and feeble (6)
7 Dance (5)
13 Storyteller (8)
16 Chinese game (3-4)
17 Severe trial (6)
19 Slightly sticky (5)
20 Obstruct (6)
22 Pompous gait (5)
24 Founder of communism (4)

The Telegraph

153

Across

1 *Watched secretly* (5)
4 *Capital of Jordan* (5)
8 Rowing device (3)
9 Characters with special powers (11)
10 Wide open (7)
12 Large group (5)
13 Hitting tool (6)
14 Mythical beast (6)
17 Mediterranean native (5)
19 Tropical fruit (7)
21 Unconquerable (11)
23 Metal container (3)
24 German city (5)
25 Garden bird (5)

Down

1 Timorous person (5)
2 Evil spirit (3)
3 Small rodents (7)
4 Get even (6)
5 Orbiting bodies (5)
6 Longing for the past (9)
7 Endurance competition (4,3)
11 Large carnivore (9)
13 Ignition device (7)
15 Male fowl (7)
16 Officer's attendant (6)
18 Great prestige (5)
20 Large body of water (5)
22 Pre-decimal coin (3)

154

Across

1 *Tall* (4)
4 *Scottish river* (3)
6 *Hurry* (3)
8 Remain calm (4,4,4)
10 Astounded (6)
12 Benefit (6)
13 Dog's name (5)
14 Tub (4)
15 Leave (4)
17 Watchful (5)
19 Incorporate (6)
21 Craned (anag.) (6)
23 Nursery school (12)
24 Greek P (3)
25 Your (archaic) (3)
26 Despatched (4)

Down

2 Nice tax (nag.) (7)
3 Funnel (6)
4 Do not admit (4)
5 Christian festival (6)
6 Laughing animal (5)
7 That's that (3,2,5)
9 Criminal (10)
11 Easy catch (5)
12 Facial hair (5)
16 Dirty (7)
17 Coming (6)
18 Zodiacal bull (6)
20 Lotto (5)
22 Unattractive (4)

The Telegraph

155

Across

1 *Caper* (5)
4 *Humorous* (5)
10 Kneecap (7)
11 Viper (5)
12 Heirloom (5)
13 Burdensome (7)
15 Thought (4)
17 Packing case (5)
19 Grass cutter (5)
22 Brawn; grumble (4)
25 Vie (7)
27 Criminal (5)
29 Cognisant (5)
30 Base (7)
31 Country; aver (5)
32 Kingdom (5)

Down

2 Of birth (5)
3 Unlawful (7)
5 Angry (5)
6 Embryonic frog (7)
7 Game (5)
8 Light boat (5)
9 Clutch (5)
14 Title (4)
16 Obligation (4)
18 Fragment (7)
20 Crime (7)
21 Sea (5)
23 Weird (5)
24 Bury (5)
26 Throw out (5)
28 Tag (5)

The Telegraph

156

Across

1 *Heart* (4)
4 *Church seat* (3)
6 *Loaned; a fast* (4)
8 Deadly (6)
9 Diminish (6)
10 Large snake (8)
11 Duelling sword (4)
12 Governmental (13)
17 Parched (4)
19 Watchful (8)
22 Abut (6)
23 Rubber (6)
24 Genuine (4)
25 Finish (3)
26 Always (4)

Down

2 Sea (5)
3 Moral, honest (7)
4 Cable tower (5)
5 Strife (7)
6 Large spoon (5)
7 Atomic (7)
10 Poisonous snake (3)
13 Shorten (7)
14 Go forward (7)
15 Preparing for cultivation (7)
16 Still (3)
18 Whimsical (5)
20 Avarice (5)
21 Female relative (5)

The Telegraph

157

Across

1 *Tall* (4)
4 *Uncertainty* (5)
8 Line of descent (8)
9 Telephone (4)
10 Unwanted emails (4)
11 Nickname of US flag (3,5)
12 Cowardly (6)
14 Breed of dog (6)
16 Retaliation (8)
19 Rain heavily (4)
20 Painful (4)
21 Sluggishness (8)
22 Austrian composer (5)
23 Member of an Indian religion (4)

Down

2 Turn of phrase (5)
3 Barbed missile (7)
4 Fear (5)
5 French painter (7)
6 Male voice (5)
7 Condiment (6)
13 The spice of life (7)
14 Exercise system (7)
15 Sitting room (6)
17 Age (5)
18 Beauty parlour (5)
19 Mischievous trick (5)

158

Across

1 *For what reason?* (3)
3 *Flan* (4)
5 *Rested; nail (anag)* (4)
8 Headlong rush (8)
10 Side (4)
11 Seaman; pitch (3)
13 Bygone (5)
14 — Hotspur FC (9)
16 Single (3)
17 Consume (3)
19 Open-mindedness (9)
21 Enough (5)
22 Equipment (3)
24 On holiday (4)
25 Christmas (8)
26 Retain (4)
27 Looked at (4)
28 Gesture; agree (3)

Down

1 Cardinal point (4)
2 Unit of time (4)
3 Compositor (10)
4 Salad plant (6)
6 Scottish city (8)
7 Propose (8)
9 Hooked claw (5)
12 Understand (10)
14 Fighting axe (8)
15 Prototype (8)
18 Pungent (5)
20 Sumptuousness (6)
22 Large oven (4)
23 Look after (4)

159

Across

1 *Knickers (abbrev.)* (6)
4 *Renter* (5)
8 *Formal dances* (5)
9 Nice gal (anag.) (7)
10 Stir (7)
11 Publicity (4)
12 Circuit (3)
14 Lazy (4)
15 Space (4)
18 Speck (3)
21 Precious (4)
23 Rail bitterly (7)
25 Performance (7)
26 Discourage (5)
27 Passé (5)
28 Believe (6)

Down

1 Optimistic (6)
2 Wasted time (7)
3 Trapped (8)
4 Elevated (4)
5 Get better (5)
6 Wealth (6)
7 Hammer (5)
13 Supplier (8)
16 Left out (7)
17 Frightened (6)
19 Legal ownership (5)
20 Strong desire (6)
22 Implied (5)
24 Stallion (4)

Across

1 *Type of frost* (4)
3 *Doomed* (4)
9 *Courage* (5)
10 Drunkard (9)
11 Wilt (5)
12 The masses (3,6)
15 Joyful (6)
17 Beat (6)
19 Complainant (9)
21 Load (5)
23 Oversee (9)
24 Blockade (5)
25 Twilight (4)
26 Benches (4)

Down

1 Intensify (8)
2 Main race (anag.) (8)
4 Operational (6)
5 Turkish viceroy (7)
6 Holy circle of light (4)
7 Halt (4)
8 Spirit (4)
13 Certain (8)
14 Goes rigid (8)
16 Revealed (7)
18 University grounds (6)
20 Roman emperor (4)
21 Blackjack (4)
22 Stench (4)

161

Across

1 *Combat* (3)
3 *Munch* (4)
5 *Mound* (4)
8 Drench (8)
10 Moist (4)
11 Tint (3)
13 Excuse (5)
14 Divert (9)
16 Ingested (3)
17 Before (3)
19 Downtrodden (9)
21 Farewell (5)
22 Forbid (3)
24 Profound (4)
25 Unmoving (8)
26 Decays (4)
27 Happy (4)
28 Hardened (3)

Down

1 Clean (4)
2 Ceremony (4)
3 Roundabout (10)
4 Tempt (6)
6 Supposes (8)
7 Crooked (8)
9 Inspection (5)
12 Paternity (10)
14 Raider (8)
15 Residue (8)
18 Majestic (5)
20 Basic (6)
22 Prejudice (4)
23 Tidy (4)

162

Across

1 *Long tooth* (4)
4 *Shrewd* (5)
8 Abandon (8)
9 Look (4)
10 Stimulus (4)
11 Moving piece of music (8)
12 Plant used for seasoning (6)
14 Packing piece used in seal (6)
16 Amount (8)
19 Catch sight of (4)
20 Ardour (4)
21 District of authority (8)
22 Attractive (5)
23 Dull (4)

Down

2 Absolute (5)
3 Bird of prey (7)
4 Dance (5)
5 Retributive justice (7)
6 Submit (5)
7 Emotional film (6)
13 Perplex (7)
14 Welsh county (7)
15 Suppose (6)
17 Affect greatly (5)
18 Hint (5)
19 Musical (5)

163

Across

1 *Compel* (5)
4 *Of great stature* (4)
8 Impresario (7)
9 40-40 in tennis (5)
10 Lustre (5)
11 — Attlee, PM (7)
13 Alcoholic spirit (6)
15 Crick's fellow geneticist (6)
17 Ready-made buildings (7)
20 Drive back (5)
22 Wait at table (5)
23 Figures of speech (7)
24 Garden tool (4)
25 Volatile liquid (5)

Down

1 Electrical safety devices (5)
2 Brazilian city (3,2,7)
3 Dressed in fur (7)
4 Pick-me-up (5)
5 Shelf (5)
6 Parliamentary address (6,6)
7 Church officer (6)
12 Statute (3)
13 Circumvent (6)
14 Lout (3)
16 Extent of ground (7)
18 Stadium (5)
19 Grab (5)
21 Stratum (5)

The Telegraph

164

Across

1 *Wear away* (4)
3 *Excite by touch* (6)
9 E.g. cherry brandy (7)
10 Buck up (5)
11 Winter sport attachment (3)
12 Using air (9)
13 Ditch (6)
14 & 24 US composer (6,4)
16 Sliding mass (9)
19 Blue (3)
21 Oust (5)
22 Sovereign's representative (7)
23 Old money in Portugal (6)
24 *See 14 Across*

Down

1 Strong winds (5)
2 Get (7)
4 Lack of ability (12)
5 Used hassock maybe (5)
6 Otalgia (7)
7 Wearing glasses (12)
8 Not confined (4)
13 Circus swing (7)
15 Notice (7)
17 Savoury jelly (5)
18 Bay (4)
20 Senior member (5)

165

Across

1 *More brawny* (7)
8 *Makers and repairers* (7)
9 Short (5)
10 Entrances (anag.); having new vitality (9)
11 Pasture (3)
12 Caterpillar (5)
13 Fashion (5)
14 Tentacled marine creature (5)
16 Rejoice intensely (5)
19 Grain (3)
20 Edible plant (9)
22 Fussy (5)
23 Well-bred (7)
24 Metal ore (7)

Down

1 With freedom of movement (6)
2 Mammal (6)
3 Rare find (anag.) (8)
4 Kigali's country (6)
5 Trouser fasteners (4)
6 Rude (6)
7 African fly (6)
13 Cooking vessel (8)
14 Untamed (6)
15 Impelling (6)
16 Mummify (6)
17 Bullet (6)
18 — and Hyde (6)
21 Forest plant (4)

166

Across

1 *Did battle* (6)
4 *Gentle taps* (6)
7 Yellow flowers (9)
9 Give praise to (4)
10 Painful spot (4)
11 Scottish river (5)
13 Person without means (6)
14 Skull in *Hamlet* (6)
15 White complexion (6)
17 Newspaper chief (6)
19 Old Scandinavian language (5)
20 Car (American) (4)
22 Jacob's brother (4)
23 Northern county (9)
24 Most painful (6)
25 Clergyman (6)

Down

1 Encouraging boost (6)
2 Cattle prod (4)
3 Clothes maker (6)
4 Convoluted (6)
5 Chances of happening (4)
6 High-pitched noise (6)
7 Reciprocal relation (9)
8 Make like the USSR (9)
11 Wrong-doer (5)
12 Large crowd (5)
15 Pieces of wood (6)
16 Shoot upwards (6)
17 OT book (6)
18 Computer distributing device (6)
21 Slimy mud (4)
22 – Morecambe (4)

The Telegraph

167

Across

1 *Naval paymaster* (6)
4 *Deviate* (4)
9 *Raves* (5)
10 Clearness (7)
11 Creditworthy (7)
12 Perfect (5)
13 Passionate (6)
15 If not (6)
18 Smallest (5)
20 Rebuke (7)
23 Merit (7)
24 Angry (5)
25 African river (4)
26 Iterate (6)

Down

1 French capital (5)
2 Festered (7)
3 Follow, result (5)
5 High spirits (7)
6 Elevate (5)
7 Sharp; severe (5)
8 Periods; bikes (6)
13 Refer (6)
14 Unaffected (7)
16 Teach (7)
17 Group of eight (5)
19 Fire-raising (5)
21 Artless (5)
22 Evict (5)

168

Across

1 *Repose* (4)
4 *Trip, visit* (4)
8 *Tirade* (4)
9 Dare (9)
11 Vitality (6)
13 Signal fires (7)
15 Scarcity (6)
16 Marine tortoise (6)
18 On a ship (6)
20 Basque ball-game (6)
22 Craftsman (7)
23 Force, pressurise (6)
25 Large spider (9)
26 Welsh emblem (4)
27 Kind; set in print (4)
28 Mail (4)

Down

2 Reverberate (4)
3 Helm (6)
4 Ditch (6)
5 Pressing (6)
6 Story (9)
7 Remain (4)
10 Makes certain (7)
12 Thought (4)
13 Atmospheric pressure measurer (9)
14 Entice (7)
17 Dutch cheese (4)
19 Dismal (6)
20 Corsair (6)
21 Portable computer (6)
23 Young male horse (4)
24 Sad to say (4)

The Telegraph

169

Across

1 *Film and TV dog* (6)
4 *Masticated* (6)
9 Sparkle (5)
10 Lack (7)
11 Farm animal (3)
12 Fragrance (5)
13 Spare time (7)
15 Itinerant (11)
19 Hobby (7)
20 Purloin (5)
21 Allow (3)
22 Eccentric (7)
24 Beginning (5)
25 Contrition (6)
26 Affluence (6)

Down

1 Sumptuous (6)
2 Witch (9)
3 Incompetent (5)
5 Antagonistic (7)
6 Victory (3)
7 Fuel (6)
8 Form of pasta (11)
14 Worldwide (9)
16 Copy (7)
17 Turmoil (6)
18 Sudden malfunction (6)
20 Pip (5)
23 Cutting remark (3)

170

Across

1 *Select* (6)
4 *Peeress* (4)
8 *Canopy* (6)
9 Thoroughfare (6)
10 Break off (5)
11 Reminder (7)
13 Paradise (4)
15 Travel across snow (3)
16 Appear (4)
18 Uproar (7)
20 Rendezvous (5)
23 Prove beyond doubt (6)
24 Hotchpotch (6)
25 Flat (4)
26 Husky (6)

Down

1 Farm worker (7)
2 Suggest (5)
3 Tale (4)
5 Stuffy (7)
6 Apply (5)
7 Hermit (7)
12 Confident (7)
14 Titular (7)
17 Mimic (7)
19 Enraged (5)
21 Keen (5)
22 Threesome (4)

171

Across

1 *Shrivels up* (7)
5 *5,280 feet* (4)
7 Headdress (5)
8 Bring on (6)
10 Chant (4)
11 Span (8)
13 Anew (6)
14 Journey (6)
17 Autocrat (8)
19 Idiotic (4)
21 Live meagrely (6)
22 Legal defence (5)
23 Serene (4)
24 Lamp (7)

Down

1 Holds out against (10)
2 Coach (7)
3 Test (4)
4 Devious (6)
5 Negotiator (8)
6 Coherent (5)
9 Prosaic; walker (10)
12 Sim space (anag) (8)
15 Greed (7)
16 Truth (religious) (6)
18 Hot drink (5)
20 Principal (4)

172

Across

1 *Hence* (4)
3 *Circular band* (4)
9 *Quantities of paper* (5)
10 African plain (9)
11 Chilly (5)
12 Helper (9)
15 Catch fire (6)
17 Breastpin (6)
19 Broadsheet, e.g. (9)
21 Collect (5)
23 Close friends (9)
24 Hearing (5)
25 London district (4)
26 Bloodsucker (4)

Down

1 Australian state (8)
2 Rebellion (8)
4 Musical dramas (6)
5 Compositor (7)
6 Moist (4)
7 Spot (4)
8 Burden (4)
13 Infirmary (8)
14 Amish car (anag.) (8)
16 Lost sin (anag.) (7)
18 Exchange (6)
20 Cougar (4)
21 Stake (4)
22 Keen (4)

The Telegraph

173

Across

4 *English astronomer* (6)
5 *Strike with head* (4)
7 Dispute noisily (7)
10 Practical joke (5)
11 Japanese dish (7)
12 Wading bird (5)
14 Law (7)
15 Cost (5)
16 Umpire (7)
20 Artificial waterway (5)
21 Significant (7)
22 Metal (4)
23 Obvious (6)

Down

1 Bias (5)
2 Kingdom (5)
3 Atrocity (7)
4 Stringed instrument (4)
6 Glittering decoration (6)
8 Mannerly (7)
9 Descriptive term (7)
10 Salted biscuit (7)
13 Fake (6)
14 Unhealthily thin (7)
17 Loosen (5)
18 Young eel (5)
19 Unite closely (4)

174

Across

1 *Heart* (4)
4 *Professor* (3)
6 *Obscure* (4)
8 Expedition (6)
9 Acquisitive (6)
10 Judgment (8)
11 Challenge (4)
12 Rain (13)
17 Exploited (4)
19 Hellish (8)
22 Fleet (6)
23 Foliage (6)
24 Submissive (4)
25 Yearning (3)
26 Memo (4)

Down

2 Harangue (5)
3 Flexible (7)
4 Condescend (5)
5 Disregard (7)
6 Fusion (5)
7 Suffer (7)
10 Deplete (3)
13 Book (7)
14 First (7)
15 Ground (7)
16 Zero (3)
18 Imbibed (5)
20 Criminal (5)
21 Proficient (5)

175

Across

1 *Flowed forth* (6)
4 *Faze, deprive of fortitude* (5)
8 Dipper or blackbird (5)
9 Grand meal (7)
10 Infuriates (7)
11 Rind (4)
12 Stitch (3)
14 Oxford's second crew (4)
15 Cunning (4)
18 Deer (3)
21 Tramp (4)
23 Faint idea (7)
25 Hard workers (7)
26 Asteroid; goddess; match (5)
27 Component of computer image (5)
28 Former West German Chancellor (6)

Down

1 E.g. made of oak (6)
2 Beggar in parable (7)
3 Praise eloquently (8)
4 Arm bone (4)
5 Rodent (5)
6 Stinging plant (6)
7 Very deep pit (5)
13 Easy victory (8)
16 Deep red (7)
17 Keep quiet! (4,2)
19 Telephone box (5)
20 Horrified (6)
22 The – , in New York (5)
24 Sudden decline (4)

176

Across

1 *Number on CD* (5)
4 *Eschew* (4)
8 Student (7)
9 Alcoholic drinks (5)
10 Abbot's deputy (5)
11 Haggle (7)
13 Musical intervals (6)
15 Loll about (6)
17 Attendant at court (7)
20 Ditch (5)
22 Gathering (5)
23 Generally (2,1,4)
24 Encounter (4)
25 E.g. toe (5)

Down

1 Bulb (5)
2 In a greedy way (12)
3 Relations (7)
4 Low woody plant (5)
5 Earthy colour (5)
6 South African city (12)
7 Medium's session (6)
12 Tool (3)
13 Conjecture (6)
14 Gentleman's form of address (3)
16 Ungraciously curt (7)
18 Nursery verse? (5)
19 Leavening agent (5)
21 Permission for absence (5)

177

Across

1 *Vulgar; not rare* (6)
5 *Expensive* (4)
8 Astound (4)
9 Etiquette (8)
10 Difficult (6)
11 Clever; vivid (6)
12 Warship (11)
15 Thread; shore (6)
17 Shrew (6)
19 Uncommunicative (8)
20 Set of cards (4)
21 Fewer; minus (4)
22 Body organ; spite (6)

Down

2 Freely available (2,3)
3 Stately home (7)
4 Asian republic (5)
5 Loincloth (5)
6 One more (7)
7 Lookalike; twofold (6)
12 Flammable gas (7)
13 Chemical element (6)
14 Light umbrella (7)
16 Goodbye (5)
17 Planet (5)
18 Trivial complaint (5)

178

Across

1 *Study* (3)
3 *Woody plant* (4)
5 *Wellington* (4)
8 Load levy (anag.) (4-4)
10 Tableland (4)
11 Beer (3)
13 ____-pocus (5)
14 Parasite (4-5)
16 Current unit (3)
17 Era (3)
19 Tom peered (anag.) (9)
21 Dirt (5)
22 Indian district (3)
24 Impel (4)
25 Noosing (8)
26 Deep valley (4)
27 Greek god (4)
28 Tow (3)

Down

1 Cold drink (4)
2 Bare (4)
3 Telecommunication system (10)
4 Looked greenly (6)
6 Outer garment (8)
7 Removal (8)
9 Panic (5)
12 Blood clot (10)
14 Widespread (3-5)
15 Final programme (8)
18 Prosper (3,2)
20 Give (6)
22 Present (4)
23 Keen (4)

The Telegraph

179

Across

1 *Transgress* (3)
3 *Cultivate; cash drawer* (4)
5 *Tardy* (4)
8 Summary; remove (8)
10 Inflamed eyelid (4)
11 Mine (3)
13 Supple (5)
14 Customers (9)
16 Female bird (3)
17 Speck (3)
19 Insipid (9)
21 Massive (5)
22 Gamble (3)
24 Genuine (4)
25 Enjoyment (8)
26 Want (4)
27 Salver (4)
28 Still (3)

Down

1 Exchange (4)
2 Bird's home (4)
3 Ended (10)
4 Find (6)
6 Height (8)
7 Weather (8)
9 The Scriptures (5)
12 Basic, simple (10)
14 Offspring (8)
15 Augment (8)
18 A willow (5)
20 Seaman (6)
22 Inter (4)
23 Exam (4)

180

Across

1 *Daze* (6)
5 *Games* (5)
9 Mediate (9)
10 Body of water (3)
11 Feline (3)
12 Innocent (9)
14 Cover (3)
16 Throw out (5)
18 Seed-bearing part of wheat (3)
19 Make sure (9)
21 Fuel (3)
22 Rage (3)
23 Proclamation (9)
25 Unpleasant (5)
26 Osier; cricket bat (6)

Down

2 Automaton (5)
3 Remarkable (7)
4 Epoch (3)
5 Strainer (5)
6 Offensive (7)
7 Sinner (12)
8 Abandonment (12)
13 Stadium (5)
15 Duke's wife (7)
17 Melodic (7)
20 Odd; card-game (5)
21 Zest (5)
24 Novel (3)

The Telegraph

181

Across

1 *Substance* (6)
5 *Openings* (5)
9 Tenancy (9)
10 Dandy (3)
11 Beverage (3)
12 Storyteller (9)
14 Floor covering (3)
16 Benefactor (5)
18 Songbird (3)
19 Snow under (9)
21 Sink (a snooker ball) (3)
22 Indian state (3)
23 Artificial language (9)
25 Respond (5)
26 Spanish dish (6)

Down

2 Capital of Ghana (5)
3 Narrowed (7)
4 Sprint (3)
5 Senior member (5)
6 Unorthodox (7)
7 Irrational belief (12)
8 Barrow boy (12)
13 Paddled boat (5)
15 Caribbean island (7)
17 Deep regret (7)
20 Cereal grass (5)
21 Jury (5)
24 Young dog (3)

182

Across

1 *Near* (4)
4 *Absorbent cloth* (5)
8 Ice lolly (US) (8)
9 Actual (4)
10 Gigantic (4)
11 Chemical element (8)
12 Spirited (6)
14 Capital of Turkey (6)
16 Songbird (8)
19 Wind instrument (4)
20 Egg-shaped (4)
21 Incautious (8)
22 Capture (5)
23 Category (4)

Down

2 Offspring; publish (5)
3 David —, painter (7)
4 Deal with (5)
5 Sorcerer (7)
6 Depart (5)
7 Book; capacity (6)
13 Onion (7)
14 Fruit (7)
15 Sturdy (6)
17 Great confusion (5)
18 Planet (5)
19 Spring flower (5)

The Telegraph

183

Across

1 *Attach (land)* (5)
4 *Lines up* (6)
9 Beaming (7)
10 Hoaxed (5)
11 Thought (4)
12 Perpetrator (7)
13 Annoy (3)
14 Junk email (4)
16 Throw (4)
18 Primate (3)
20 Cowered (7)
21 Just (4)
24 Of a town (5)
25 Building (7)
26 Send me (anag.); corrects (6)
27 Upright (5)

Down

1 Fearful (6)
2 Prod (5)
3 Medical photo (1-3)
5 Be wavy (8)
6 Referees (7)
7 Tranquillise (6)
8 Glue (5)
13 Conceived of (8)
15 Flexible (7)
17 Impeach (6)
18 Viper (5)
19 Fervent (6)
22 Tolerate (5)
23 Quote (4)

184

Across

1 *Violent criminal* (4)
4 *Objective* (3)
6 *Imbibe* (3)
8 Clean (5,3,4)
10 UK native (6)
12 Secret romance (6)
13 Sentimental (5)
14 Undertaking (4)
15 Similar to (4)
17 Design (5)
19 Predatory insect (6)
21 Praised (6)
23 At times (4,2,1,5)
24 Take to court (3)
25 Joke (3)
26 Regretted (4)

Down

2 Flower people (7)
3 Lizards (6)
4 Regrettably (4)
5 Alter (6)
6 Cuttlefish ink (5)
7 Correspondents (3,7)
9 I mess about (anag.) (10)
11 Forbidden fruits (2-3)
12 Spring month (5)
16 Give free rein to (7)
17 Excavating (6)
18 Sire (6)
20 Alcove (5)
22 Be suspended (4)

The Telegraph

185

Across

1 *Falsehood* (3)
3 *Durable* (5)
6 *Wrath* (3)
8 Obscures (5)
9 Hang (7)
10 Subsequently (10)
12 Snooze (3)
15 Competition (4)
17 Story (4)
18 Epoch (3)
22 Sophistication (10)
25 Nominate (7)
26 Thick (5)
27 Gender (3)
28 Truck (5)
29 Illuminated (3)

Down

1 Toilet (8)
2 Testimony (8)
3 Examined (6)
4 Dangerous (6)
5 Hurry (6)
6 Notion (4)
7 Whirlpool (4)
11 Informer (3)
13 Fatherly (8)
14 Conscious (8)
16 Stray (3)
19 Antenna (6)
20 Winner (6)
21 Fatal (6)
23 Overtake (4)
24 Pinnacle (4)

The Telegraph

186

Across

1 *Trolley wheel* (6)
4 *Consider carefully* (5)
8 Deserve (5)
9 Race aim (anag.) (7)
10 With a leg either side (7)
11 Leave out (4)
12 Expanse of water (3)
14 Footwear (4)
15 Gust (4)
18 Pose (3)
21 In addition (4)
23 Previously (7)
25 Goal (7)
26 Burnt remains (5)
27 Tall grasses (5)
28 Spectres (6)

Down

1 Military action (6)
2 Scrape (7)
3 Sketches (8)
4 Unwanted plant (4)
5 Expression (5)
6 Enthusastic (6)
7 Gets weaker (5)
13 Near (8)
16 Air journeys (7)
17 Impede (6)
19 Doctrine (5)
20 Emergency (6)
22 Merry frolic (5)
24 Tasks (4)

187

Across

1 *Hurtful comment* (4)
3 *Point the finger at* (6)
9 Earmark (7)
10 Crouching position (5)
11 Sailor (3)
12 Mobile guard (9)
13 Neglectful (6)
14 Elated (6)
16 Italian composer (9)
19 Dwarf (3)
21 Parcel out (5)
22 Grain store (7)
23 Oil carrier (6)
24 Darling (4)

Down

1 Cap (5)
2 Platform (7)
4 Worldly (12)
5 Normal (5)
6 Obtains by coercion (7)
7 Type of pancake (5,7)
8 Preliminary race (4)
13 Glowing (7)
15 Cow (7)
17 Synthetic material (5)
18 African country (4)
20 Reception area (5)

The Telegraph

188

Across

1 *Vehemence* (5)
4 *Having on* (7)
8 Japanese warrior (7)
9 Offence taken (5)
10 Ruth's mother-in-law (Old Testament) (5)
11 Reticence (7)
13 Spanish artist (4)
15 Chinese philosophical system (6)
17 Sufferer (6)
20 Yemeni port (4)
22 An analgesic (7)
24 Improvised musically (5)
26 Tartan cloth (5)
27 Female comedian (7)
28 Takes it easy (7)
29 Powered by sun (5)

Down

1 Finely woven (4-3)
2 Famous lover (5)
3 Insects (7)
4 Fanciful thoughts (6)
5 Sufficiently (5)
6 Judicial enquiry (7)
7 'Trainspotters' (5)
12 Possess (4)
14 Former Gulf country, Muscat and — (4)
16 Eccentric person (7)
18 Hurts (7)
19 Westminster area (7)
21 True skin (6)
22 Dance playfully (5)
23 A-to-Z listing (5)
25 Relating to region (5)

189

Across

1 *Muscle* (4)
4 *Nerd (anag.)* (4)
8 ___ *-a-ling* (4)
9 London theatre (9)
11 Zodiacal bull (6)
13 Young hen (7)
15 Mole (6)
16 Built with a slope (6)
18 Odeons (anag.); knotty (6)
20 Boredom (6)
22 More vain (7)
23 Sheep's flesh (6)
25 Vessel for boiling water (3,6)
26 Trickle (4)
27 Support (4)
28 Young sheep (4)

Down

2 Test (4)
3 Dirty (6)
4 Diminish (6)
5 Tureen (anag.) (6)
6 Dilapidation (9)
7 Don't teach your grandmother to suck ___ (4)
10 Ran (7)
12 Type of melon (4)
13 State (9)
14 Having trouble (2,1,4)
17 Empty out (4)
19 ___ Hemingway (6)
20 Large bird (6)
21 Of teeth (6)
23 Bungle (4)
24 Thin (4)

190

Across

1 *More substantial* (7)
5 *Entitlement* (5)
8 Native American dwelling (5)
9 Hat decoration (7)
10 Steam engine worker (7)
11 Gradually become thinner (5)
12 False rumour (6)
14 Horse-drawn cab (6)
17 Plane driver (5)
19 Utter nonsense (7)
22 Sport played on ice (7)
23 Dull, insipid (5)
24 Magnetic unit (5)
25 Utterly confuse (7)

Down

1 Recurring pattern (5)
2 Analgesic drug (7)
3 Part of intestines (5)
4 Retract opinion (6)
5 Soft Italian cheese (7)
6 Hold tightly (5)
7 Mathematical proposition (7)
12 Person who imitates (7)
13 Greek wine (7)
15 Sharp blade (7)
16 Japanese ruler (6)
18 Baits, decoys (5)
20 Taken as read (5)
21 Greek underworld (5)

191

Across

1 *Express disapproval* (4)
4 *Alarm* (5)
8 Kindred (8)
9 Average (4)
10 Expensive; beloved (4)
11 Sloth (8)
12 Figurine (6)
14 Emerge (6)
16 Plentiful (8)
19 Awful (4)
20 In want; below par (4)
21 Needed (8)
22 Damp (5)
23 Pitcher (4)

Down

2 Lay to rest (5)
3 Fawning (7)
4 Bearcat (5)
5 Continuous (3-4)
6 Freight (5)
7 Apprehend (6)
13 Fit of temper (7)
14 Ancient (7)
15 Tallied (6)
17 Stall (5)
18 Pungent (5)
19 Steer; trip (5)

192

Across

1 *Hog* (3)
3 *Thwack* (5)
6 *Cunning; insect* (3)
8 Nurse; female goat (5)
9 Horseshoe-smith (7)
10 Ground tremor (10)
12 Beer (3)
15 Cudgel (4)
17 Be aware of (4)
18 Unhappy (3)
22 Callisthenics (10)
25 Pirate (7)
26 Prickly plants (5)
27 Aged (3)
28 Overweight (5)
29 Epoch (3)

Down

1 Acridity, piquancy (8)
2 Munificent (8)
3 Reaping implement (6)
4 Inundation (6)
5 'I've found it!' (Greek) (6)
6 Just; fete (4)
7 Tale; thread (4)
11 European moose (3)
13 Surround (8)
14 Nazi symbol (8)
16 Sack (3)
19 Energy converter (6)
20 False (6)
21 Human mind/soul (6)
23 Reverberate (4)
24 Poke (4)

The Telegraph

193

Across

1 *Vera —; King's —* (4)
4 *Swindle* (3)
6 *Transgress* (3)
8 Picture; example (12)
10 Scallywag (6)
12 Hiccup (6)
13 Hungarian wine (5)
14 Splendid; penalty (4)
15 Lofty; unlikely (4)
17 Welcome (5)
19 Vulgar (6)
21 Pay attention (6)
23 Hair oil (12)
24 Female sheep (3)
25 Recede (3)
26 Summit (4)

Down

2 Russian president (7)
3 Chewy confection (6)
4 Musical; animals (4)
5 Almost (6)
6 Fast; bird; writer (5)
7 Unconcerned (10)
9 Cost-effective (10)
11 Goods vehicle (5)
12 Auctioneer's hammer (5)
16 Aerial (7)
17 Grating (6)
18 Excellent (6)
20 Correspond (5)
22 Wounding remark (4)

194

Across

7 *Riviera resort* (6)
8 *Unmanageable sort* (6)
10 African river (7)
11 Snooker table fabric (5)
12 Remove from herd (4)
13 Female fox (5)
17 Bedspread (5)
18 Region (4)
22 Toss (5)
23 Admiring statement (7)
24 Fix (6)
25 Deadly (6)

Down

1 Trashy (Yiddish) (7)
2 Deviation, irregularity (7)
3 Fruit (5)
4 Bird (7)
5 Mark (5)
6 Self-congratulate (5)
9 Good-humouredness (9)
14 Prison cell (7)
15 Shortage (7)
16 Antelope (7)
19 Edible internal parts (5)
20 Abandon (5)
21 Make broader (5)

The Telegraph

195

Across

1 *Stage* (5)
4 *Robber* (5)
8 *Chopper* (3)
9 Famous people (11)
10 Assuage (anag.) (7)
12 Gnashers (5)
13 Buy back (6)
14 Females (6)
17 Stains (5)
19 Cadged (7)
21 Mysterious (11)
23 Is able to (3)
24 Mucky (5)
25 Made a mistake (5)

Down

1 Chooses (5)
2 Suffer (3)
3 Hug (7)
4 Clans (6)
5 Fool (5)
6 Tying (9)
7 Long seats (7)
11 Subordinate (9)
13 Court (7)
15 Disciple (7)
16 Off course (6)
18 Japanese dish (5)
20 Fear (5)
22 Exclude (3)

196

Across

1 *Man courting* (6)
4 *Smallholder, e.g.* (6)
7 Toll road (8)
9 Catching (7)
12 Adores (5)
13 Incompetent (5)
15 Worth (5)
16 Overturn (5)
17 Keen (5)
19 South African region (5)
20 In name only (7)
24 Lowering of rank (8)
25 Accusation (6)
26 Tension (6)

Down

1 Outpost (10)
2 Not respectful (10)
3 Facing (8)
4 Cut and run (4)
5 Source (4)
6 Regular (4)
8 Leg joint (4)
10 Twist together (10)
11 Rules of thumb (10)
14 Traitor (8)
18 Blood (4)
21 Urge (4)
22 Exploiter (4)
23 Edging tool (4)

The Telegraph

197

Across

1 *Autocrat* (4)
5 *College official* (4)
7 South American country (7)
8 French resort (8)
10 Support, aid (4)
12 Potato (4)
14 Opening (8)
16 Medical institution (8)
17 Daintily pleasing (4)
18 Gas (4)
19 Homeless wandering (8)
22 Hat (7)
23 Fling (4)
24 Hard wood (4)

Down

1 Burial site (4)
2 German industrial region (4)
3 Rejoicing (8)
4 Grill (4)
5 Of ruling families (8)
6 Amphibian (4)
9 Better (7)
11 Irregular (7)
13 Stupidity (8)
15 Extol (8)
18 Immediately after (4)
19 Opinion (4)
20 Relative (4)
21 Part of egg (4)

The Telegraph

198

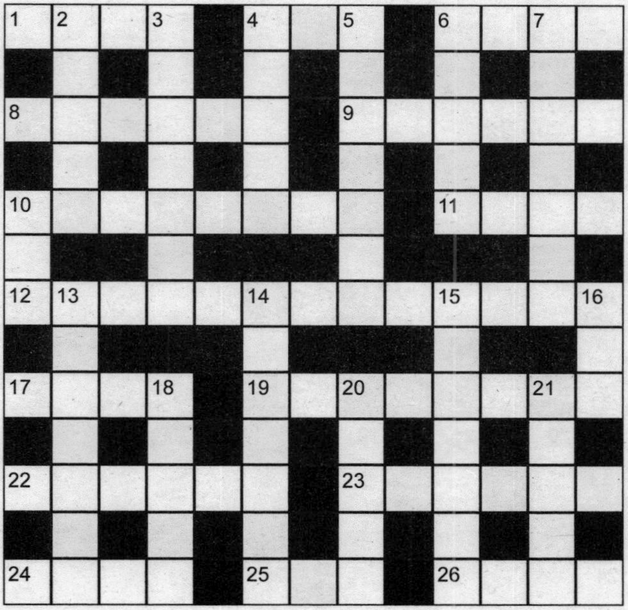

Across

1 *Exhale* (4)
4 *Coach* (3)
6 *Step* (4)
8 Untamed (6)
9 Beginning (6)
10 Abstinent (8)
11 Complicated (4)
12 Dismay (13)
17 Filth (4)
19 Panorama (8)
22 Elementary (6)
23 Surpass (6)
24 Geek (4)
25 Discern (3)
26 Coil (4)

Down

2 Livid (5)
3 Firesides (7)
4 Complain (5)
5 Engorged (7)
6 Ground (5)
7 Farewell (7)
10 Twitch (3)
13 Aperture (7)
14 Rapid (7)
15 Current (7)
16 Snare (3)
18 Lukewarm (5)
20 Overweight (5)
21 Doctrine (5)

199

Across

1 *Card game* (6)
4 *Figure* (6)
7 Informal talk (8)
9 US state, city (3,4)
12 Arms and legs (5)
13 50:50 probability (5)
15 Type of tea (5)
16 S. American country (5)
17 OT patriarch (5)
18 Rub out (5)
19 End of a spar (7)
23 Breaking free (8)
24 Pal (6)
25 Set in motion (6)

Down

1 Oddly (10)
2 Panel-game host (10)
3 Apology for interruption (6,2)
4 Short communication (4)
5 Numerous (4)
6 Always (4)
8 No maestro (anag.) (9)
10 Duty (10)
11 Like breeches (4-6)
14 Plans (8)
20 Slightly open (4)
21 Pantomime female (4)
22 Peruse (4)

200

Across

1 *Sauce* (7)
5 *Subsequently* (5)
8 Bit of computer image (5)
9 Labour (7)
10 Living in water (7)
11 Dullard (5)
12 Slightly windy (6)
14 Read casually (6)
17 Racecourse (5)
19 Discourteous (7)
22 Funny (7)
23 Branch of philosophy (5)
24 Beach (5)
25 Treat with consideration (7)

Down

1 Tenth Greek letter (5)
2 Feel of material (7)
3 Composer Gustav (5)
4 Coup (6)
5 Hero and – (7)
6 Sequence (5)
7 Ease (7)
12 Supplementary regulations (3-4)
13 Spooky beings (7)
15 Noisy dispute (7)
16 Recreational runner (6)
18 Reject (5)
20 Records (5)
21 Old coin (5)

The Telegraph

201

Across

1 *Small room* (4)
4 *Causes a strain on* (5)
8 *Blossoming* (2,6)
9 Sea dog (4)
10 Suggestion (4)
11 One expected to lose (8)
12 Chess piece (6)
14 Drive away (6)
16 Polar explorer (8)
19 Fierce temper (4)
20 Curved structure (4)
21 Short rest (8)
22 Arboreal primate (5)
23 Move gently (4)

Down

2 Applause (5)
3 Court case (7)
4 Dismissed (5)
5 Unsuccessful competitor (4-3)
6 Succession of shots (5)
7 Lowly ranked officer (6)
13 Cotton cloth (7)
14 Completely mad (7)
15 Long document (6)
17 Edible mushroom (5)
18 Serious, restrained (5)
19 Islamic decree (5)

202

Across

1 *Drag* (4)
4 *Period of time* (3)
6 *Worker* (4)
8 — *Twist* (6)
9 *Sir* (6)
10 Most annoyed (8)
11 Printing mistake (4)
12 Account of one's problems (4-4,5)
17 Fair (4)
19 Flowering tree (8)
22 Remnant (6)
23 China clay (6)
24 Court order (4)
25 Coal scuttle (3)
26 Bobcat (4)

Down

2 Exhausted (3,2)
3 Prised (7)
4 Funeral hymn (5)
5 Siberian city (7)
6 Lift up (5)
7 One has nil chance of success (2-5)
10 Volcanic dust (3)
13 Rock containing water (7)
14 Unfasten a door (7)
15 Upheaval (7)
16 US sweet potato (3)
18 Understood (5)
20 Cooked in an oven (5)
21 League (5)

203

Across

1 *Arrogant* (7)
5 *Sect* (4)
7 *Household job* (5)
8 Mention; imply (6)
10 Slender (4)
11 Reed instrument (8)
13 Ostentatious (6)
14 Precise (6)
17 Eternal (8)
19 Too (4)
21 Coax (6)
22 Discuss, contend (5)
23 Dregs (4)
24 Show (7)

Down

1 Conjurer's incantation (5-5)
2 Ideal; imaginary (7)
3 Take notice of (4)
4 Annual (6)
5 Quickness (8)
6 Freighted (5)
9 Writing materials (10)
12 Diligent; scholarly (8)
15 Unlawful (7)
16 Certainly (6)
18 Rub out (5)
20 Girl (4)

204

Across

1 *Silent* (4)
4 *Cash drawer* (4)
8 *Tardy* (4)
9 Rejoice (9)
11 Zodiac sign, the Bull (6)
13 French composer (7)
15 Aniseed drink (6)
16 Motive; argue (6)
18 Gently boil (6)
20 Flemish painter (6)
22 Cloudy (7)
23 Thick soup (6)
25 Ornate (9)
26 Price (4)
27 European river (4)
28 Connect (4)

Down

2 Second-hand (4)
3 Number; team (6)
4 Inert (6)
5 Epistle (6)
6 Court lawyer (9)
7 Muddle; canteen (4)
10 Tranquil (7)
12 Musical work (4)
13 Playwright (9)
14 Pastille; rhombus (7)
17 Bird's home (4)
19 Staggered (6)
20 Eraser (6)
21 Cask (6)
23 Treaty (4)
24 Stupefy (4)

205

Across

1 *American nut* (5)
4 *Masticates* (5)
10 Scene (7)
11 Intended (5)
12 Play (5)
13 Belted (7)
15 Plenty (4)
17 Understanding (5)
19 Way in (5)
22 Reduce (pain) (4)
25 Happy (7)
27 Sovereign (5)
29 Getting older (5)
30 Quantities (7)
31 Consent (5)
32 Famous racecourse (5)

Down

2 Bonus (5)
3 Creatures (7)
5 Mortal (5)
6 Climate (7)
7 Aides (anag.) (5)
8 North African country (5)
9 Office (5)
14 Employs (4)
16 Candid (4)
18 Directing (7)
20 Anxious (7)
21 Huge body of water (5)
23 Book of maps (5)
24 Impel (5)
26 Large bird of prey (5)
28 Jargon (5)

The Telegraph

206

Across

1 *Compel* (5)
4 *In what place?* (5)
8 Boom; bellow (7)
9 Male relative (5)
10 Belgium-born actress (6,7)
11 Filled with horror (6)
12 Pester (6)
15 A tense (6,7)
18 Ascend (5)
19 Line touching curve (7)
20 Record; agree (5)
21 Praise (5)

Down

1 Islamic law ruling (5)
2 Crazy (5,3,5)
3 Infinite (7)
4 Creditable (6)
5 Provide (5)
6 Reassurance (13)
7 Racket sport (6)
11 Influence (6)
13 Put in order (7)
14 Indifference (6)
16 Revolt (5)
17 Amount to (5)

The Telegraph

207

Across

- **1** *Behave* (3)
- **3** *Part of skull* (3)
- **5** *Fury* (4)
- **7** Tremor (5)
- **8** Published (6)
- **10** Part of eye (4)
- **11** Personal magnetism (8)
- **13** Slumped (6)
- **14** Savage (6)
- **17** Clear (8)
- **19** Remedy (4)
- **21** Prophesier (6)
- **22** Origins (5)
- **23** Yield (4)
- **24** However (3)
- **25** Aver (3)

Down

- **1** Assented (10)
- **2** Dealing (7)
- **3** Boo (4)
- **4** Importance (6)
- **5** Hold back (8)
- **6** Reckon (5)
- **9** Incautiously (10)
- **12** Second-rate (8)
- **15** Rowdy (7)
- **16** Opportune (6)
- **18** Cleanse (5)
- **20** Guts (4)

The Telegraph

208

Across

1 *Weird* (5)
4 *Chase* (4)
7 *E.g. oak* (4)
8 Extrovert (8)
9 Great landmass (9)
10 Stain (3)
12 Spies (6)
14 A suit (6)
16 Watch closely (3)
18 Mysterious (9)
21 Composer, perhaps (8)
22 Quote (4)
23 Closed (4)
24 Passenger (5)

Down

1 Forsaken (7)
2 Effort (8)
3 Experienced (5)
4 Head covering (4)
5 Childminder (5)
6 Reek (6)
11 Poised (8)
13 Insult (anag.) (6)
15 Chirrup (7)
17 Juvenile (5)
19 Doomed person (5)
20 Regimen (4)

209

Across

1 *Standard* (3)
3 *Edge* (3)
5 *Curve* (4)
7 Team (5)
8 Compiler (6)
10 Malevolent (4)
11 Fortress (8)
13 Appeared (6)
14 Infer (6)
17 Obsolete (8)
19 Remedy (4)
21 Drink (6)
22 Goad (5)
23 Remain (4)
24 Summit (3)
25 Boy (3)

Down

1 Ownership (10)
2 Mundane (7)
3 Impolite (4)
4 Lose (6)
5 Lawyer (8)
6 Cooks (5)
9 Attentive (10)
12 Persistence (8)
15 Peculiar (7)
16 Fraud (6)
18 Entice (5)
20 Pace (4)

The Telegraph

210

Across

1 *Crow's cry* (3)
3 *Policeman's round* (4)
5 *Arguments* (4)
8 *Restrain* (8)
10 Profound (4)
11 Before (3)
13 Hindu social class (5)
14 Spanish dance (4,5)
16 Cuttlefish secretion (3)
17 Make a choice (3)
19 Hypocritical (9)
21 Sun-powered (5)
22 Little devil (3)
24 Crazy (4)
25 Carry over (8)
26 Irritate (4)
27 Tackle (4)
28 Mmm, delicious! (3)

Down

1 Lawsuit (4)
2 Rub clean (4)
3 Deterrent fencing (6,4)
4 Take in (6)
6 Galosh (8)
7 Seven-piece band (8)
9 Municipal (5)
12 Cruise ship (5,5)
14 Kind of lager (8)
15 Emaciated (8)
18 Choice (5)
20 Turn aside (6)
22 Dubious (4)
23 Esplanade (4)

The Telegraph

211

Across

1 *South Korean capital* (5)
4 *Irritated* (7)
8 In the last month (abbrev.) (3)
9 Extinct bird (3)
10 Attack; start (5)
11 Sophia –, Italian actress (5)
12 29 in astronomy (7)
15 Stake in advance (4)
17 Go to bed (6)
19 Protector (6)
22 Designated place (4)
24 Groups of six (7)
26 Metrical feet (5)
28 Angry (5)
30 Era (3)
31 Task (3)
32 Article (anag.) (7)
33 Frolic (5)

Down

1 Dirty conditions (7)
2 Fish-eating animal (5)
3 In sheet form (7)
4 Biblical mount (6)
5 Ruth's mother-in-law (5)
6 Affirmative reply (3)
7 Jettison (5)
13 Piquancy (4)
14 Yorkshire river (3)
16 Bird's home (4)
18 Levy (3)
20 Young cows (7)
21 Drool (7)
23 Country (6)
24 Slider on snow (5)
25 Happening (5)
27 John –, ex-PM (5)
29 Curve (3)

The Telegraph

212

Across

1 *Antelopes* (4)
3 *Dark-complexioned* (7)
8 Sweater (6)
9 Dominion (6)
10 Annual publication (8)
11 No-winner result (4)
12 Hearsay (6)
15 Ten-year span (6)
17 Leave; resign (4)
19 On unauthorised ski slope (3-5)
22 USA's southern neighbour (6)
23 Fame (6)
24 Become rigid (7)
25 Seaside platform (4)

Down

1 Cloth for bandage (5)
2 Cricket officials (7)
4 Ruined (7)
5 Fast (5)
6 American university (7)
7 Therefore (4)
13 Luxurious (7)
14 Incite (7)
16 Red wine (7)
18 Stealer (5)
20 Type of plant (4)
21 Tall building (5)

The Telegraph

213

Across

1 *Puncture* (5)
4 *Jump* (4)
8 *Tune* (3)
9 Barren area (9)
10 Male voice (4)
11 Undo sandals (8)
12 Work unit (3)
13 Irish city (6)
14 Stink (6)
16 Enemy (3)
17 Old meets (anag.) (8)
18 Lower leg (4)
20 Large church (9)
21 Undergarment (3)
22 Bloodsucker (4)
23 Irked (5)

Down

1 Poster (7)
2 Peevishness (12)
3 NZ bird (4)
4 Logs in (anag.) (6)
5 Passable (8)
6 Toy (4-2-3-3)
7 Cutting tool (4)
11 Vase (3)
12 US physicist (8)
14 Sward (3)
15 Parliamentary record (7)
16 Polecat (6)
17 Scoff at (4)
19 Eastern European (4)

The Telegraph

214

Across

1 *Cascade of water* (4)
4 *Small songbird* (3)
6 *For you and me* (4)
8 Steal (6)
9 *The Great* – (novel) (6)
10 Rotating-wing aircraft (8)
11 College (familiarly) (4)
12 Not working (13)
17 Blackleg (4)
19 Frivolous (8)
22 Mouth (slang) (6)
23 Official writer (6)
24 By mouth (4)
25 Human being (3)
26 Underground source (4)

Down

2 Parting greeting (5)
3 Launch (of rocket) (4-3)
4 Towelling material (5)
5 Harbour craft (7)
6 Freely available (2,3)
7 German measles (7)
10 Assistance (3)
13 More disgusting (7)
14 Quack cure (7)
15 Get too big for (7)
16 Sixth note (3)
18 Aromatic herb (5)
20 Norwegian playwright (5)
21 Female oracle (5)

The Telegraph

215

Across

1 *Bronze coin* (5)
4 *Taut; strained* (5)
10 Gauge (7)
11 Permit (5)
12 Bloodsucker (5)
13 Segregate (7)
15 Journey (4)
17 Japanese capital (5)
19 Perfect (5)
22 Gentlewoman (4)
25 Mistake (7)
27 Maritime (5)
29 Sea (5)
30 Spot, watch (7)
31 Scatter (5)
32 Artificial fibre (5)

Down

2 Rub out (5)
3 Risqué (7)
5 Muse of poetry (5)
6 Dried grape (7)
7 Plentiful (5)
8 Weird (5)
9 Proprietor (5)
14 Slide (4)
16 Actor's part (4)
18 Rich, luxuriant (7)
20 Family line (7)
21 Loathe (5)
23 Fire-raising (5)
24 Foreign (5)
26 Thick (5)
28 Zodiac sign (5)

The Telegraph

216

Across

1 *Manufacturer* (5)
4 *Lass* (4)
7 *Seize* (4)
8 Tongue (8)
9 Contribute money (9)
10 Pig-pen (3)
12 Enfeeble (6)
14 Incorporate (6)
16 Perform (3)
18 First (9)
21 Gamp (8)
22 Cripple (4)
23 Fete (4)
24 Cleave (5)

Down

1 Magnitude (7)
2 Memento (8)
3 Monarch; measurer (5)
4 Pummel (4)
5 Vision (5)
6 Empower (6)
11 Unusual (8)
13 Almost (6)
15 Tooth doctor (7)
17 Punctuation mark; butterfly (5)
19 Accumulate (5)
20 Operatic song (4)

217

Across

1 *Wharf* (4)
4 *Complete* (5)
8 Supporter (8)
9 Flying toy (4)
10 Treaty (4)
11 Built-in (8)
12 Malaysian garment (6)
14 Attractive (6)
16 Paltry (8)
19 Of sound mind (4)
20 Revolve (4)
21 Quiet (8)
22 Adversary (5)
23 Very small (4)

Down

2 Dark (5)
3 Wide open (7)
4 Merit (5)
5 Large plant, symbol of strength (3,4)
6 Consumed (5)
7 Musical composition (6)
13 Crime (7)
14 Parade (7)
15 Language (6)
17 Course (5)
18 Insinuate (5)
19 Strict (5)

218

Across
1 *Shopping centre* (4)
4 *Make fun of* (5)
8 Go to ruin (8)
9 Combat to settle a row (4)
10 Indistinct (4)
11 Personal (8)
12 Well drilling plant (3,3)
14 Dutch city (6)
16 Expedient (5-3)
19 Opinion (4)
20 Fair (4)
21 Body of ideas (8)
22 Shellfish (5)
23 Creature of disputed existence (4)

Down
2 Narrow lane (5)
3 Bird (7)
4 English river (5)
5 Belly (7)
6 Vote into office (5)
7 North-east African (6)
13 Italian cheese (7)
14 Worry (7)
15 Dynamism (6)
17 Take by force (5)
18 Simulate (5)
19 Male servant (5)

219

Across

1 *A month* (3)
3 *Remedies* (5)
6 *Family* (3)
8 *Grovel* (5)
9 Fighter (7)
10 Decorative (10)
12 Valet (3)
15 Volcano (4)
17 Pig meat (4)
18 Wildebeest (3)
22 Changeover (10)
25 Dessert wine (7)
26 Compass (5)
27 Beam (3)
28 Avarice (5)
29 Cheek (3)

Down

1 Bugs (8)
2 Longing (8)
3 Tower (6)
4 Arguing (6)
5 Flow (6)
6 Fuse (4)
7 Never (a) (4)
11 Drink; lick (3)
13 Theoretical (8)
14 Superficial (4-4)
16 Emmet (3)
19 Encouraging (6)
20 Insecure (6)
21 In rows (6)
23 Arab ruler (4)
24 Nervous (4)

The Telegraph

220

Across

1 *Royal House* (7)
5 *Gorse* (5)
8 Crucial (5)
9 Crash (7)
10 Dream-like (7)
11 Overweight (5)
12 Arrest (6)
14 Bear witness (to) (6)
17 Discovered (5)
19 Disaster (7)
22 Demonstrate (7)
23 Bird of prey (5)
24 Merry frolic (5)
25 Salted away (7)

Down

1 Spouses (5)
2 Unspoilt (7)
3 Work out (5)
4 Memory (6)
5 Quarrel (4,3)
6 Elevate (5)
7 Himalayan peak (7)
12 Strongboxes (7)
13 Able to be heard (7)
15 Came out (7)
16 Sew (6)
18 Guide (5)
20 Stadium (5)
21 Give way (5)

The Telegraph

221

Across

4 *Affair* (6)
5 *Entrance* (4)
7 Town district (7)
10 Extensive (5)
11 Capricious (7)
12 Macabre fiend (5)
14 Style (7)
15 Phrygian king (5)
16 Humourless (2-5)
20 African country (5)
21 Recount (7)
22 Expel (4)
23 Cowardly (6)

Down

1 Hoard (5)
2 Outcast (5)
3 Opaque watercolour paint (7)
4 Injure with claws (4)
6 Seasoned stew (6)
8 Disloyalty (7)
9 Month in Muslim calendar (7)
10 Smoking accessory (7)
13 Harridan (6)
14 Pouch for infant (7)
17 Nucleus of servicemen (5)
18 Number of cattle (5)
19 Daze (4)

The Telegraph

222

Across

1 *Distribute* (5)
4 *Relatives* (7)
8 Dash (3)
9 Swine (3)
10 Hump (5)
11 Pallid (5)
12 Graceful (7)
15 Tender (4)
17 Verbal (6)
19 Zealous (6)
22 Cipher (4)
24 Obstacle (7)
26 Doctrine (5)
28 Madness (5)
30 Pertinent (3)
31 Vase (3)
32 Greatest (7)
33 Soothes (5)

Down

1 Outstrip (7)
2 Hacienda (5)
3 Outlay (7)
4 Fisherman (6)
5 Titled (5)
6 Infirm (3)
7 Sugary (5)
13 Guide (4)
14 Beer (3)
16 Formerly (4)
18 Paddle (3)
20 Performance (7)
21 News (7)
23 Flowery (6)
24 Jolts (5)
25 Likeness (5)
27 Uniform (5)
29 Snooze (3)

223

Across

1 *Money gained* (6)
4 *Fold* (5)
8 Stringed instrument (5)
9 Displaced exile (7)
10 Showy ornaments (7)
11 Waistcoat (in US) (4)
12 Scotsman's cap (3)
14 Tiny bird (4)
15 Dash (4)
18 24 hours (3)
21 Dissolute man (4)
23 Extent of land (7)
25 Make comprehensible (7)
26 Ape (5)
27 Waste pipe (5)
28 Swarm of insects (6)

Down

1 Drink (6)
2 Overwhelm by force (7)
3 Desolate territory (8)
4 Praise in advertisements (4)
5 Bird of prey (5)
6 XX (6)
7 Icy condensation (5)
13 Calm rite (anag.) (8)
16 Fantastic (7)
17 Chum (6)
19 Signs of boredom? (5)
20 Building for worship (6)
22 Tenth Greek letter (5)
24 Daybreak (4)

224

Across

1 *Herb* (5)
5 *Absence of war* (5)
8 Slow (music) (5)
9 Denims (5)
10 Having too few for meeting (9)
11 Beard of plant (3)
12 One playing for time (11)
15 Irish elves (11)
19 Atmosphere (3)
20 Blandished (9)
22 Came to consciousness (5)
23 Synthetic material (5)
24 Raise in praise (5)
25 Laconic (5)

Down

1 Indian mausoleum (3,5)
2 Longs (6)
3 Hamlet's place (8)
4 One-off (6)
5 Venetian explorer (4)
6 Attack (6)
7 Boundary (4)
13 In plentiful supply (8)
14 Get back (8)
16 Public square (6)
17 Bringer of news (6)
18 Taste with enjoyment (6)
20 Renown (4)
21 Canvas shelter (4)

The Telegraph

225

Across

1 *Pound (slang)* (6)
5 *Italian meat sauce* (4)
8 *Was dressed in* (4)
9 Frivolous in speech (8)
10 Small hole (6)
11 Loud rock band (3,3)
12 State of chaos (11)
15 Rich cake (6)
17 Austrian composer (6)
19 Family servant (8)
20 Weaving apparatus (4)
21 Price (4)
22 Cry of success (6)

Down

2 Tusk material (5)
3 Moscow landmark (7)
4 Overhaul (ship) (5)
5 Indian coin (5)
6 Cotton cloth (7)
7 Small restaurant (6)
12 Inactive drug (7)
13 Horse-like (6)
14 Asthmatic's aid (7)
16 Precise (5)
17 TV detective (5)
18 Literature from the internet (1-4)

The Telegraph

226

Across

1 *Dried grass* (3)
3 *Crush* (5)
6 *Tug* (3)
8 Injury (5)
9 Prop up (7)
10 Stranded (4,3,3)
12 Ox (3)
15 Baby's biscuit (4)
17 Animal skin (4)
18 Second-year sheep (3)
22 One who takes care of wildlife (10)
25 Windpipe (7)
26 Door-fastening (5)
27 Intelligence (3)
28 Rest (5)
29 Small amount (3)

Down

1 Hedge tree (8)
2 Most youthful (8)
3 Hawker (6)
4 Incorporate (6)
5 Pay (6)
6 Ballet skirt (4)
7 Toil (4)
11 Bark (3)
13 Persevere (4,2,2)
14 The cards (anag.) (8)
16 Small barrel (3)
19 Collect (6)
20 Item (6)
21 Responsive (6)
23 Casserole (4)
24 Reality (4)

The Telegraph

227

Across

1 *Great!* (5)
4 *Mean* (6)
9 Thick (5)
10 The best (7)
11 Beg, implore (7)
12 Hold, cleave (5)
14 Female sheep (3)
15 Feline (3)
16 Jewel (3)
18 Headgear (3)
21 Lucid (5)
22 Barge (7)
23 Resolute (7)
25 Surpass (5)
26 Food store (6)
27 Postpone (5)

Down

1 Abrupt (6)
2 Pierce (9)
3 Staggered (6)
5 Instruction (6)
6 Forest tree (3)
7 Harm (6)
8 Consider (11)
13 The same (9)
17 Scribble (6)
18 Invent (6)
19 Concurred (6)
20 Soft hat with indented crown (6)
24 Song; ventilate (3)

228

Across

1 *Curb* (6)
4 *Dulcet* (5)
8 Truism (5)
9 Non-attendance (7)
10 Italian red wine (7)
11 Jetty (4)
12 Father (3)
14 Pleased (4)
15 Acme (4)
18 Epoch (3)
21 Simple (4)
23 Tramp, trudge (7)
25 Extremities, ends (7)
26 Vex (5)
27 Larceny (5)
28 Grain (6)

Down

1 Bough (6)
2 Beginning; first letter (7)
3 Soft drink (8)
4 Window-frame (4)
5 Boredom (5)
6 Supposition (6)
7 Swift (5)
13 Info collection (8)
16 Cost (7)
17 Half-dozen in a group (6)
19 Garret (5)
20 Dr — and Mr Hyde (6)
22 Attend; start to play tennis (5)
24 Present (4)

229

Across

- **1** *Factory* (4)
- **4** *Armed conflict* (3)
- **6** *Wharf* (4)
- **8** Scallywag (6)
- **9** Without lumps (6)
- **10** Passionate (8)
- **11** Stuart monarch (4)
- **12** Offence (13)
- **17** Male deer (4)
- **19** Disruption (8)
- **22** Spanish rice dish (6)
- **23** Claim (6)
- **24** Remain (4)
- **25** Shack (3)
- **26** Cautious (4)

Down

- **2** Furious (5)
- **3** Reading desk (7)
- **4** Irish playwright (5)
- **5** Cockade (7)
- **6** Allocation (5)
- **7** — Vivaldi, composer (7)
- **10** Check (3)
- **13** Withdraw, take back (7)
- **14** Hungarian stew (7)
- **15** Of little depth (7)
- **16** Nothing (3)
- **18** Ravine (5)
- **20** Centre (5)
- **21** Vexation (5)

230

Across

1 *Bovine animals* (6)
5 *Stuart monarch* (4)
8 Rotate; ride (4)
9 Insolvent (8)
10 Bauble (6)
11 Legal (6)
12 Sudden disaster (11)
15 Bad writing (6)
17 European river (6)
19 Mexican hat (8)
20 Partly open (4)
21 Tax (4)
22 Long list (6)

Down

2 Large enough (5)
3 This evening (7)
4 Arm joint (5)
5 Pointed missile (5)
6 Roman sea god (7)
7 Fisherman (6)
12 Spiralling wind (7)
13 Vendor (6)
14 Long narrow flag (7)
16 Convent (5)
17 Amusing (5)
18 Muscle (5)

The Telegraph

231

Across

1 *Catcalled* (6)
5 *Oak, e.g.* (4)
8 *An agate* (4)
9 By and large (8)
10 Colonnade (6)
11 Let off (6)
12 Pretend (4,7)
15 Pressure line (6)
17 Heart (sl.) (6)
19 Recounts (8)
20 Deeds (4)
21 Hairless (4)
22 Serious; gloomy (6)

Down

2 Secret (5)
3 Abs; beer (3-4)
4 Flamenco, perhaps (5)
5 Manage to find (5)
6 Obscure (7)
7 Trial (6)
12 Make-up (7)
13 Scold (6)
14 Cry out (7)
16 Drilled; fed up (5)
17 Jobs to do (5)
18 Go in (5)

The Telegraph

232

Across

1 *Conflict* (5)
4 *Steal (sl.)* (4)
8 *Turned, sour* (3)
9 Vegetated (9)
10 Agreement (4)
11 Unparalleled (8)
12 Pot (3)
13 Wrecked (6)
14 Gambol (6)
16 Hawthorn (3)
17 Think about (8)
18 Mark on skin (4)
20 Retinue (9)
21 Parrot (3)
22 Give way (4)
23 Complain (5)

Down

1 Cleaver (7)
2 Loving (12)
3 Flexible tube (4)
4 Tidy up (6)
5 Perverse (8)
6 Horse race (12)
7 Poems (4)
11 Writing block (3)
12 Foot treatment (8)
14 Distant (3)
15 Present (7)
16 Threat (6)
17 Work party (4)
19 Edge of road (4)

The Telegraph

233

Across

1 *Place* (3)
3 *Secure* (4)
5 *Whisker* (4)
8 Supplier (8)
10 Minus (4)
11 Finish (3)
13 Chose (5)
14 Rest (9)
16 Poem (3)
17 Sped (3)
19 False (9)
21 Pseudonym (5)
22 Misery (3)
24 Diplomacy (4)
25 Norm (8)
26 Masticate (4)
27 Dread (4)
28 However (3)

Down

1 Bound (4)
2 Court (4)
3 Doubtfulness (10)
4 Ruddy (6)
6 Opening (8)
7 Occupant (8)
9 Single (5)
12 Precursor (10)
14 Sentimental (8)
15 Average (8)
18 Thespian (5)
20 Dress (6)
22 Cautious (4)
23 Correct (4)

234

Across

1 *Disapproving sound* (3)
3 *Toot* (4)
5 *Get up* (4)
8 Time (8)
10 Aussie birds (4)
11 Front of shoe (3)
13 Cowboy show (5)
14 Arrogant (9)
16 Undivided (3)
17 Pouch (3)
19 Glasses with handle (9)
21 Wear, rub (5)
22 Goal (3)
24 Mar (4)
25 Nudge (8)
26 Foreboding (4)
27 Satiate (4)
28 Tree (3)

Down

1 Kick (4)
2 Previously (4)
3 Blockbuster (10)
4 Bighead (6)
6 Bigheaded (8)
7 Nestle (8)
9 Punctuation mark (5)
12 As a rule (10)
14 Musical composition (8)
15 Defeatist (8)
18 Make amends (5)
20 Display (6)
22 Rim (4)
23 Bongo (4)

235

Across

1 *Tricked* (6)
4 *Possessing* (6)
7 Empty (8)
9 Church bell (7)
12 Group of soldiers (5)
13 Sudden alarm (5)
15 Chosen ones (5)
16 Keen (5)
17 Office furniture (5)
18 Having sharp prongs (5)
19 Well-founded (7)
23 With skill (8)
24 Odds and ends for sale (6)
25 Not ruffled (6)

Down

1 Gossip (4,3,3)
2 From Naples (10)
3 Kitted out (8)
4 Cattle (4)
5 Church area (4)
6 Socially unacceptable (3-1)
8 Blemished (9)
10 Of language (10)
11 Very optimistic (6-4)
14 Pit of filthy water (8)
20 Beige (4)
21 Horse (4)
22 Be idle (4)

236

Across

1 *Young salmon* (4)
3 *Amuses* (7)
8 Wrecker (6)
9 Hostility (6)
10 Dagger (8)
11 Mediterranean island (4)
12 Dense forest (6)
15 Film cartoonist (6)
17 Insect (4)
19 Finnish capital (8)
22 Setting (6)
23 Light wind (6)
24 Pardon (7)
25 Stream (4)

Down

1 Industrial equipment (5)
2 Socialism emblem (3,4)
4 To sum up (2,1,4)
5 Cutter (5)
6 Even-tempered (7)
7 Conspiracy (4)
13 Radioactive element (7)
14 Use up (7)
16 Paint in dots (7)
18 Group of lions (5)
20 Indolent (4)
21 Inuit canoe (5)

The Telegraph

237

Across

1 *Summit* (4)
4 *Disquiet* (6)
8 Oust (8)
9 Dip (4)
10 Board game (4)
11 Relax (6)
13 Scottish city (6)
16 Computer device (5)
17 Plump (5)
19 Go away! (6)
22 Reflect (6)
24 Invertebrate (4)
25 Retired (4)
26 City runs (anag.) (8)
27 Loan shark (6)
28 Starting point in darts (4)

Down

2 Blow up (7)
3 Horn (6)
4 Incorrect (6)
5 Woden (anag.) (5)
6 Alternative option (6,6)
7 Storm cloud (12)
12 Type of lamp (4)
14 Boss on a shield (4)
15 Canine (3)
18 Charm (7)
20 Rubber (6)
21 Cook too long (6)
23 Navigation aid (5)

238

Across

1 *Animal skins* (4)
3 *Spun around* (7)
7 *Was dressed in* (4)
8 Duelling weapon (4)
9 Financial checker (7)
10 Printer's proof (6)
13 Name for parrot (5)
14 Drive out (4)
16 Fuel carrier (6)
18 Roofing material (6)
20 Short note (4)
21 French river (5)
22 Cleaning devices (6)
25 Rotary motor (7)
26 Somewhat demented (4)
27 Funeral party (4)
28 Enthusiasm (7)
29 Low ground (4)

Down

1 Transported goods (7)
2 Dandy (5)
3 Hard wood (4)
4 Very detailed (2-5)
5 Small digit (6,3)
6 Bowler hat (5)
11 Places of interest (9)
12 Long ago (4)
15 Pack away (4)
17 Retired professors (7)
19 Captive (7)
21 Arrangement (3-2)
23 Called to phone (5)
24 Chopped (4)

239

Across

1 *Short sleeps* (4)
4 *Plunders; fires* (5)
8 Mishap (8)
9 Raw hide (4)
10 Portent (4)
11 Gift (8)
12 Hot spring (6)
14 Sweet (6)
16 Whole (8)
19 Tax (4)
20 Woodwind instrument (4)
21 Replied (8)
22 Name; heading (5)
23 Reign (4)

Down

2 Foreign (5)
3 Slim (7)
4 The Devil (5)
5 Chief; money (7)
6 Volley (5)
7 Busy (6)
13 Wise (7)
14 Kitchen sideboard (7)
15 Respect (6)
17 Go round (5)
18 Rub out (5)
19 Reside (5)

240

Across

1 *Pain-relieving opium extract* (7)
5 *Cash* (5)
8 Equestrian; added clause (5)
9 Headache pill (7)
10 Frighten (9)
12 Playing card (3)
13 Mexican revolutionary (6)
14 Groups of singers (6)
17 Male offspring (3)
18 Everlasting (9)
20 Distraught (7)
21 Tool for grasping, lifting (5)
23 Housey-housey (5)
24 Unfeigned (7)

Down

1 Deserve (5)
2 Stick (3)
3 Offer for rent (4,3)
4 Leisurely (music) (6)
5 Sugar tree (5)
6 Story (9)
7 Americans (informal) (7)
11 Contrite (9)
13 Energetic (7)
15 Encourage (7)
16 Brawl (6)
18 Courtyard (5)
19 Flavour (5)
22 Maiden-named (3)

The Telegraph

241

Across

4 *E.g. bass* (6)
5 *Needy* (4)
7 Fashionable (2,5)
10 Happen (5)
11 Type of film (7)
12 Brawl (5)
14 Lancashire town (7)
15 Native of New Zealand (5)
16 Live (at) (7)
20 Nonsense (5)
21 Most intimate (7)
22 Attractive man (4)
23 Detest (6)

Down

1 Fund (5)
2 Planet (5)
3 Trip (7)
4 Rational (4)
6 Piece of bacon (6)
8 Authentic (7)
9 Public schoolboy (7)
10 Caucasian republic (7)
13 Extravagant (6)
14 Highway robber (7)
17 Sweeping item (5)
18 Hackneyed (5)
19 Small seabound place (4)

The Telegraph

242

Across

1 *Juicy fruit* (5)
4 *Scottish sheepdog (alternative spelling)* (5)
10 Put on clothes (7)
11 Easy elegance (5)
12 Say (5)
13 Midday meals (7)
15 Critically examines (4)
17 Darling (5)
19 Way in (5)
22 Relax (4)
25 Most pale (7)
27 Non-conformist (5)
29 Type of water lily (5)
30 Smoothing (7)
31 In a strange way (5)
32 One escorts people to seats (5)

Down

2 Incident (5)
3 Watch (7)
5 Instrument (5)
6 Tanned skin (7)
7 Smell (5)
8 Grown-up (5)
9 Needs (anag.) (5)
14 Employs (4)
16 Narrowly watches (4)
18 Left out (7)
20 Timid (7)
21 Reside (5)
23 Classical (5)
24 Grows languid (5)
26 Picture frame (5)
28 Kickback (5)

The Telegraph

243

Across

1 *Hawthorn* (3)
3 *Osculate* (4)
5 *Conservative* (4)
8 Directly; neat (8)
10 Italian volcano (4)
11 A wee dram (3)
13 Allow to enter (3,2)
14 A tiny bit (9)
16 Unit of electrical resistance (3)
17 Hostelry (3)
19 Ready-to-wear (3-3-3)
21 Belief system (5)
22 Regret (3)
24 Destroy (4)
25 Remorseless (8)
26 Annoy (4)
27 Hide; rain (4)
28 Set (table) (3)

Down

1 Haze (4)
2 Mongolian tent (4)
3 Order of chivalry (10)
4 Train (6)
6 Run faster than (8)
7 Longing (8)
9 Sense; affect (5)
12 Explosive situation (10)
14 Wizard (8)
15 Majestic (8)
18 Link (5)
20 Catlike (6)
22 Actual (4)
23 Catch sight of (4)

244

Across

1 *Estimate* (5)
5 *Put out (flames)* (5)
8 Hate (5)
9 Drive-in accommodation (5)
10 Teeny-weeny (4-5)
11 Light meal (3)
12 Pun (4,2,5)
15 Irrelevant reply (3,8)
19 Self-importance (3)
20 Heir (9)
22 Gain knowledge (5)
23 Body (5)
24 Customs (5)
25 Title-holder (5)

Down

1 Sense; courage (8)
2 Snare (6)
3 Water at the mouth (8)
4 Therapist (abbrev.) (6)
5 Dull (4)
6 Area of Ireland (6)
7 Simple (4)
13 1815 battle (8)
14 Sailing ship (8)
16 Honey (6)
17 Doubtful (6)
18 Stay (6)
20 Pretence (4)
21 Consumes (4)

245

Across

1 *Tickle* (4)
4 *Steersman* (3)
6 *Greek letter* (3)
9 *London Olympics supremo* (3)
10 Benefactor (5)
11 Frequently (5)
12 Dance for two (3,2,4)
15 Thick sweet dairy product (9,4)
19 Clothes fastener (5,4)
21 Snapshot (5)
22 Guide (5)
24 Submachine-gun (3)
25 Fabrication (3)
26 Stain (3)
27 Jug (4)

Down

2 Treachery (7)
3 Boundary (5)
4 Rook (3)
5 Copied (7)
6 Glue (5)
7 Golf club (4)
8 Frozen mass (7)
13 Follow (5)
14 Crash-helmet (4,3)
16 Interpret (7)
17 Gatecrash (7)
18 Waken (5)
20 Junket (5)
21 Become tiresome (4)
23 Weed (3)

The Telegraph

246

Across

1 *Exceeded; invaded* (7)
5 *Uncertainty* (5)
8 Supply (5)
9 European river (7)
10 Assessment (9)
12 Baked dish (3)
13 Climax (6)
14 Food fish (6)
17 Greek letter (3)
18 Scottish capital (9)
20 Down payment (7)
21 Cautionary light (5)
23 Reverie (5)
24 Countersign (7)

Down

1 Musical drama (5)
2 Flightless bird (3)
3 Italian painter (7)
4 One going naked (6)
5 Training (5)
6 Disliked (9)
7 Tease (7)
11 Juicy fruit (9)
13 Retrieved (cricket) (7)
15 Scold (7)
16 Small (6)
18 English racecourse (5)
19 Swarm (5)
22 Public house (3)

The Telegraph

247

Across

1 *Rowing team* (4)
5 *Dynamism* (4)
7 Italian composer (7)
8 Predict (8)
10 Expert (4)
12 Burden (4)
14 Sheath for sword (8)
16 Meat cut (8)
17 Grudging admiration (4)
18 Brought up (4)
19 Riding breeches (8)
22 Wise utterances (7)
23 Furnace (4)
24 Cab (4)

Down

1 Applaud (4)
2 Bathrobe (4)
3 Slandered (8)
4 Cathedral town? (4)
5 African country (8)
6 Game with clubs (4)
9 Farmer (7)
11 Always (7)
13 Air force unit (8)
15 Canine breed (8)
18 Bed; rubbish (4)
19 French saint (4)
20 Mail (4)
21 Indian garment (4)

The Telegraph

248

Across

1 *Severely criticised* (6)
4 *Atmosphere* (4)
8 Unimportant matters (6)
9 Approve officially (6)
10 Cover for bed (5)
11 Spanish port (7)
13 Traditional story (4)
15 Rod for snooker (3)
16 Silly (4)
18 Examined (7)
20 Sharp (5)
23 Loose skirt (6)
24 Hooter (6)
25 Large pond (4)
26 Diversions (6)

Down

1 Court offence (7)
2 New (5)
3 Dash (4)
5 Not tested (7)
6 Fearsome (5)
7 Gentle winds (7)
12 Amount of land (7)
14 Fish (7)
17 Asinine (7)
19 Dog (5)
21 Seat (5)
22 Omit (4)

The Telegraph

249

Across

1 *In what way?* (3)
3 *Awkward* (8)
9 Teacher (5)
10 City on the Avon (7)
11 Domesticated pig (3)
13 Whirlpool (9)
14 Furtive (6)
16 Felt hat (6)
18 Petty theft (9)
20 Weep (3)
22 Naval officer (7)
23 Command (5)
25 Get the better of (8)
26 Friend (3)

Down

1 Snag (5)
2 Humour (3)
4 Pill (6)
5 Under discussion (2,5)
6 Infamous (9)
7 Quandary (7)
8 Ghastly (4)
12 Diving bird (9)
14 Adult female voice (7)
15 Formula to be proved (7)
17 Seafarer (6)
19 Greek god of love (4)
21 Gemstone (5)
24 Decline (3)

250

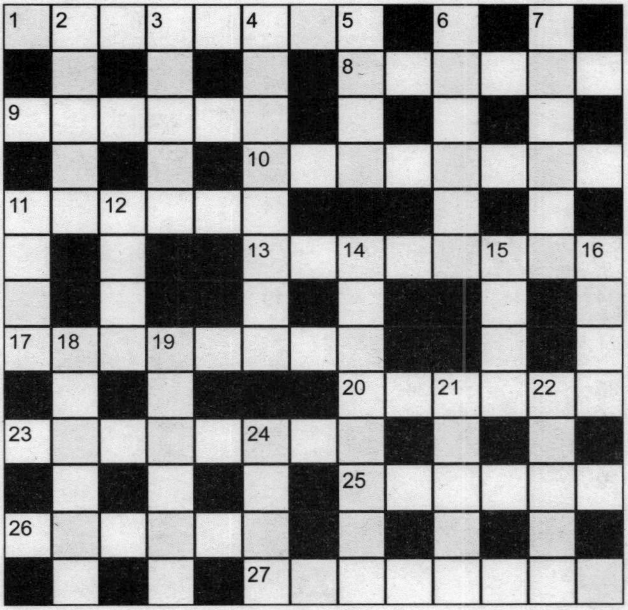

Across

1 *Business* (8)
8 *Wraps* (6)
9 Public notice (6)
10 Most uneven (8)
11 Stand still! (6)
13 Patching (anag.) (8)
17 Figure of speech (8)
20 Safety device in a car (6)
23 Large aeroplane (5,3)
25 A flowing in (6)
26 Agreement (6)
27 Very large (4-4)

Down

2 Rank (5)
3 What rubbish (2,3)
4 Economise (8)
5 Jacob's twin (4)
6 Seal; mark of prestige (6)
7 Liquid part of blood (6)
11 Business organisation (4)
12 Egress (4)
14 Tory gain (anag.) (8)
15 Association (4)
16 Stopper (4)
18 Horsy (6)
19 Lie in wait (6)
21 William II (5)
22 Humming (5)
24 Rubbish (4)

251

Across

1 *Lowest rank of peerage* (5)
4 *Ship's middle* (5)
10 Hand reader (7)
11 Stroll (5)
12 The same (5)
13 Captivate (7)
15 Unsightly (4)
17 Body trunk (5)
19 To the point (5)
22 Elderly (4)
25 'A'; 'the'; thing (7)
27 Furious (5)
29 Faint (5)
30 Acute (7)
31 Kingdom (5)
32 Climb; balance (5)

Down

2 Distribute (5)
3 Threatening (7)
5 Separate (5)
6 Day of worship (7)
7 Digging implement (5)
8 Purloin (5)
9 Quay (5)
14 Sort (4)
16 Objective (4)
18 Result (7)
20 Fatuous (7)
21 Untrue (5)
23 Arabian sprite (5)
24 Gem (5)
26 Waterway (5)
28 Cancel, revoke (5)

The Telegraph

252

Across

1 *Cosmos* (8)
5 *Large town* (4)
8 Stylishness (8)
9 Legend (4)
11 Law-making (11)
14 Extinct NZ bird (3)
16 Spanish table wine (5)
17 Vast age; eternity (3)
18 Forged (11)
21 Two-masted ship (4)
22 Recommend; lawyer (8)
24 Brink (4)
25 Regular (8)

Down

1 Second-hand (4)
2 Perfect (5)
3 Overstate (10)
4 Dry (of wine) (3)
6 Visualise (7)
7 Longing (8)
10 Corpse-like (10)
12 Scrub (5)
13 Friendly (8)
15 Droll (7)
19 Pope's triple crown (5)
20 Tear; hire (4)
23 Two-person act (3)

The Telegraph

253

Across

1 *Murderer* (6)
5 *Coastline curve forming a bay* (5)
9 Change the position of (9)
10 Fix; equip (3)
11 Hatchet (3)
12 Advantageous (9)
14 Concealed (3)
16 Educate (5)
18 Fasten (3)
19 Tried (9)
21 Metallic element (3)
22 Public house (3)
23 Poverty-stricken (9)
25 Diving water bird (5)
26 Repartee (6)

Down

2 Icon (5)
3 Biggest (7)
4 Race (3)
5 Rear; variety (5)
6 Clothing item (7)
7 Camaraderie (12)
8 Awe-inspiring (12)
13 Braid (5)
15 Easing of hostility (7)
17 Roman emperor (7)
20 Tree (5)
21 Subject; motif (5)
24 Gist (3)

254

Across

1 *Knitting stitch* (4)
3 *Narrow clefts* (8)
9 Sweetening agent (5)
10 Whiskey (7)
11 Sphere (3)
13 Mischievous fairy (9)
14 Outcast (6)
16 Central courtyard (6)
18 The very same (9)
20 Doze (3)
22 Thrash (7)
23 Bog; inundate (5)
25 Sailor (8)
26 Refute (4)

Down

1 Pasta sauce (5)
2 Mat (3)
4 Quaff (6)
5 Extinguish (4,3)
6 Uprising (9)
7 Word with same meaning (7)
8 Curved structure (4)
12 Spanish city (9)
14 Pedestals (7)
15 Aerial (7)
17 Agree (6)
19 Fail to keep (4)
21 Opium flower (5)
24 Playing card (3)

The Telegraph

255

Across

1 *Went under* (4)
3 *Cerise* (6)
8 Scope (7)
9 Gun (5)
10 Reminder (5)
11 Alfresco (4-3)
12 Hostelry (6)
14 Brandy (6)
17 Dress for bed (7)
19 Asian country (5)
21 Approaches (5)
22 Large wave (7)
23 Be there (6)
24 Cock-crow (4)

Down

1 The best (6-2-4)
2 Wanderer (5)
3 Universe (6)
4 Spooky (5)
5 Abstain; chorus (7)
6 Run; calling (6)
7 Loss in value (12)
13 Tramp (7)
15 Hateful (6)
16 Fired-up (6)
18 Savour (5)
20 Play (5)

256

Across

1 *Cuban capital* (6)
5 *Cry loudly* (4)
8 Footwear (4)
9 Think (8)
10 Investigated (6)
11 Sensitive (6)
12 Out of keeping (11)
15 Powerful (6)
17 Tight, mean (6)
19 News report (8)
20 Miss out (4)
21 Flex (4)
22 Attempts (6)

Down

2 Hate (5)
3 Bitter (7)
4 Having weapons (5)
5 Conductor's wand (5)
6 See (7)
7 Newspaper boss (6)
12 Butt in (7)
13 Deny (6)
14 Menacing (7)
16 Eyed lustily (5)
17 Burn lightly (5)
18 Mucky (5)

The Telegraph

257

Across

1 *Ascend* (5)
4 *Overfill* (4)
7 *Suspended* (4)
8 Fragrant (8)
9 Intolerant (9)
10 Epoch (3)
12 Fisherman (6)
14 Euphoric (6)
16 Wager (3)
18 Periphery (9)
21 Majesty (8)
22 Peak (4)
23 Hooligan (4)
24 Fragment (5)

Down

1 Sentimental (7)
2 Awkward (8)
3 Commerce (5)
4 Drench (4)
5 Article (5)
6 Swivel (6)
11 Drool (8)
13 Woken (6)
15 Intense (7)
17 World (5)
19 Disrobe (5)
20 Cosy (4)

The Telegraph

258

Across

1 *Rule* (5)
4 *Become wearisome* (4)
7 Beat (4)
8 French city (8)
9 Stew-pan (9)
10 Extra in cricket (3)
12 Barrack (6)
14 Awkward (6)
16 Fitting (3)
18 US state (3,6)
21 Italian dessert (8)
22 Implement (4)
23 Gala (4)
24 Aristocrat's territory (5)

Down

1 Art form (7)
2 Japanese city (8)
3 African country (5)
4 Gambit (4)
5 Loot, dosh (5)
6 Air travel fatigue (3,3)
11 Absurdly impractical (8)
13 Sickening (6)
15 Nut tree (7)
17 Group of lions (5)
19 Template (5)
20 Stare (4)

The Telegraph

259

Across

1 *Brands (e.g. of cars)* (7)
5 *Thomas —, author* (4)
7 — Williams, theologian (5)
8 Purchased (6)
10 Fencing sword (4)
11 Fits of temper (8)
13 Sign for unqualified driver (1-5)
14 Carnival (6)
17 Fearless (8)
19 Leap (4)
21 Underground chamber (6)
22 Fad (5)
23 School near Slough (4)
24 Insincere excuse (7)

Down

1 Wonderful (10)
2 Unfair treatment (3,4)
3 Bone in arm (4)
4 Underpass (6)
5 Large pile (8)
6 Indian statesman (5)
9 Steep slope (10)
12 Fish (8)
15 Tubular food item (7)
16 Abduct (6)
18 Modify (5)
20 Unit of area (4)

260

Across

1 *Her raft (anag.)* (7)
5 *Herb* (5)
8 Polish monetary unit (5)
9 Xylophone-like instrument (7)
10 Something found (9)
12 Belief system (3)
13 Fairness (6)
14 Maths diagrams (6)
17 Task (3)
18 Hand-held weapons (5,4)
20 Lancastrian's enemy (7)
21 Inert gas (5)
23 Evade (5)
24 Given means of support (7)

Down

1 Unnnerved (5)
2 Greek letter (3)
3 Storage in barn (7)
4 'Desert Fox' (6)
5 Wait (5)
6 Jewish fast day (3,6)
7 Dutch humanist (7)
11 Slept (9)
13 Relished (7)
15 At ease (7)
16 Fortified building (6)
18 Look happy (5)
19 Church council (5)
22 At this moment (3)

The Telegraph

261

Across

1 *Master of —* (4)
5 *Extremities* (4)
7 *Wine flasks* (7)
8 Very hot day (8)
10 Wrongful act (4)
12 Drop of rain (4)
14 Rectory (8)
16 Emphasised (8)
17 Destroy selectively (4)
18 Added to (4)
19 Deterioration (8)
22 Dais (7)
23 Lots (4)
24 Spoilt child (4)

Down

1 Hebrew prophet (4)
2 Blemish (4)
3 Rich vase (anag.) (8)
4 A long way off (4)
5 Coteries (anag.) (8)
6 Preservative (4)
9 Chief city (7)
11 Normal (7)
13 Exchequer (8)
15 L = Lima, e.g. (8)
18 Prudish (4)
19 Hyphen (4)
20 Burial-vault (4)
21 Amphibian (4)

262

Across

1 *Chew on* (4)
3 *Quickly turn pages* (5)
7 *Rise up* (4)
8 Guarantee financially (10)
9 Easily led (4)
12 Mischievous ghost (11)
13 Inquisitive (5)
15 Vehicle crash (5)
19 Red and tough (anag.); battleship (11)
21 Persian ruler (4)
23 Theatre promoter (10)
24 Young deer (4)
25 More strange (5)
26 Financial asset (4)

Down

1 Bad humour (10)
2 Grapple (7)
3 In poor taste (6)
4 For men and women (6)
5 Makes tea (5)
6 Festival (4)
10 European volcano (4)
11 High honour (10)
14 Fizzy drink (4)
16 Meaningless talk (7)
17 Out of shape (6)
18 Make loved (6)
20 Horned pachyderm (5)
22 Deception (4)

The Telegraph

263

Across

1 *Arrive* (4)
3 *Entreaty* (4)
9 *Intended* (5)
10 Musical group (9)
11 Claw (5)
12 Persist (9)
15 Emasculated man (6)
17 Gilt brass (6)
19 Infamy (9)
21 Ape (5)
23 An artificial language (9)
24 Additional (5)
25 Ogle (4)
26 Quarry (4)

Down

1 Casino worker (8)
2 Pasta tubes (8)
4 Written communication (6)
5 Non-professional (7)
6 Bucket (4)
7 Stupefy (4)
8 Gala (4)
13 Chief, boss (8)
14 Meddler (8)
16 Hide (7)
18 Russian plain (6)
20 Singular, infrequent (4)
21 Encounter (4)
22 Dumb (4)

264

Across

1 *Beer and lemonade drink* (6)
4 *Ogle* (4)
8 Scanty (6)
9 Disinter (6)
10 Equestrian (5)
11 Runner (7)
13 Expectant (4)
15 Male title (3)
16 Close, stingy (4)
18 Passionate (7)
20 Waterway (5)
23 Breathe in (6)
24 Dwell (6)
25 Appear (4)
26 Grave (6)

Down

1 Young tree (7)
2 Concur (5)
3 Feat (4)
5 Stepped formation (7)
6 Pay; mail (5)
7 100 years (7)
12 Affected; supposed (7)
14 Rubbish (7)
17 Desert (7)
19 Without (5)
21 Passageway (5)
22 Threesome (4)

265

Across

1 *Large bag* (4)
4 *Cheerful* (5)
8 Slayer of snakes (8)
9 Diplomacy (4)
10 Acidic (4)
11 Mirth (8)
12 Genial (6)
14 Spanish dance (6)
16 Italian cheese (8)
19 Fair (4)
20 Capital of Peru (4)
21 Tepid (8)
22 Begin (5)
23 Seaweed (4)

Down

2 Annoyance (5)
3 Expertise (4-3)
4 Thieve (5)
5 Unprocessed (7)
6 Sailing boat (5)
7 Sullen (6)
13 Brazilian dance (7)
14 Capital of Thailand (7)
15 Tourist centre (6)
17 Zodiac sign (5)
18 Divide (5)
19 Precious stone (5)

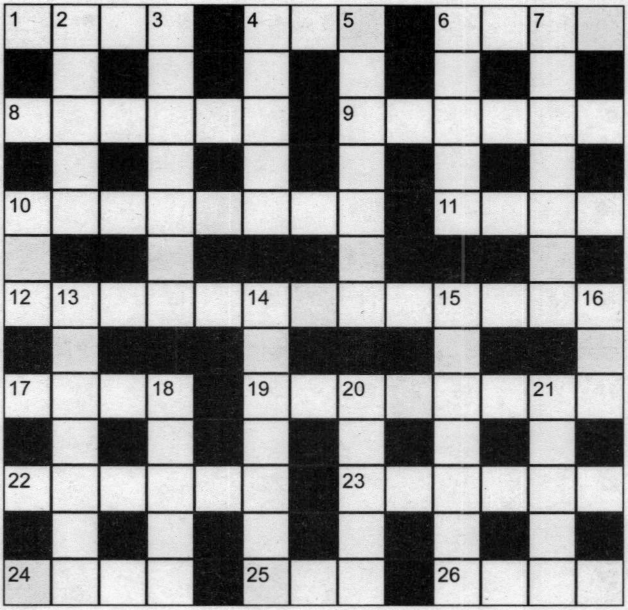

266

Across

1 *Dearth* (4)
4 *Slip up* (3)
6 *Bewilder* (4)
8 *Farmer's hook* (6)
9 Boisterous laugh (6)
10 Run-down (8)
11 Insurrection (4)
12 Shambles (4,9)
17 Second-hand (4)
19 Gathering (8)
22 Breakfast cereal (6)
23 Unwell (6)
24 Gaggle (4)
25 Day before (3)
26 Dash (4)

Down

2 Similar (5)
3 Number puzzles (7)
4 Ogle (3,2)
5 Yacht or boat races (7)
6 Postpone (5)
7 Ardent (7)
10 Flop (3)
13 Unheard-of (7)
14 See liar (anag.) (7)
15 Mishandled (7)
16 Scottish river (3)
18 Attractive (5)
20 Shear closely (5)
21 Recluse (5)

267

Across

1 *Record; memo* (4)
3 *Peddling* (7)
8 Abut (6)
9 Edible root (6)
10 Liaises (8)
11 Shack (4)
12 Protect (6)
15 Emissary (6)
17 Male of whale (4)
19 Attendance (8)
22 Booths (6)
23 Romans (anag.) (6)
24 Teach (7)
25 Poems (4)

Down

1 Jog (5)
2 Cheat on (3-4)
4 Spray can (7)
5 Prestige (5)
6 Incipient (7)
7 Biting fly (4)
13 Frequented (7)
14 Lodge (7)
16 Gathered (7)
18 Purple (5)
20 A peer (4)
21 Harvests (5)

268

Across

1 *Bug, rile* (5)
4 *Alien* (7)
8 *Yes* (3)
9 And not (3)
10 Goddess of love (5)
11 Perhaps (5)
12 Implement (7)
15 Catch sight of (4)
17 Absorb (6)
19 Mind; soul (6)
22 – Guinness (4)
24 Rescue (7)
26 Villain (5)
28 Show indifference (5)
30 Consumed (3)
31 Personal (3)
32 Engross (7)
33 Hostelry (5)

Down

1 Frightened (7)
2 Destitute (5)
3 Northern Americans (7)
4 Enthuse (4,2)
5 Variety show (5)
6 Hostelry (3)
7 Of the nose (5)
13 Sort (4)
14 Thus (3)
16 Male deer (4)
18 Mousse (3)
20 Shriek (7)
21 Unending (7)
23 Emissary (6)
24 Japanese dish (5)
25 Fury (5)
27 Crow (5)
29 Male sheep (3)

The Telegraph

269

Across

1 *Fasten* (3)
3 *Make a mistake* (3)
5 *Rowing boat* (4)
7 Prankster (5)
8 Hue (6)
10 Fatty tissue (4)
11 Sickly sentimentality (8)
13 Reconnaissance unit (6)
14 Sole (6)
17 Canadian city (8)
19 Pacific islands (4)
21 Journey (6)
22 Disprove (5)
23 Join (4)
24 Gist (3)
25 Long period (3)

Down

1 Of local interest (6-4)
2 Disregard (7)
3 Uniform (4)
4 Florid (6)
5 Thin wire (8)
6 Customary (5)
9 Asian republic (10)
12 Food connoisseur (8)
15 Raise trivial objections (7)
16 Tilt to one side (6)
18 Loop in rope (5)
20 Food (4)

270

Across

1 *Disorder* (4)
4 *Silence* (4)
8 *Encounter* (4)
9 Unoccupied (9)
11 Dynamism (6)
13 Location (7)
15 Bustle (6)
16 Manoeuvre (6)
18 Drawing (6)
20 Wreckage (6)
22 Vacation (7)
23 Assess (6)
25 Soothe (9)
26 Lattice (4)
27 Worry (4)
28 Aspiration (4)

Down

2 Begrudge (4)
3 Frisson (6)
4 Enthusiastic (6)
5 Noiseless (6)
6 Region (9)
7 Linger (4)
10 Occupied (7)
12 Inquires (4)
13 Oversee (9)
14 Windpipe (7)
17 Expense (4)
19 Gaffe (6)
20 Forthright (6)
21 Exile (6)
23 Bottom (4)
24 Pace (4)

The Telegraph

271

Across

1 *Wise Men's gift* (5)
4 *Provide food etc* (5)
10 Ornamental style (7)
11 Absolute (5)
12 Follow (5)
13 African country (7)
15 Dark sauce (4)
17 Greek philosopher (5)
19 Indian king (5)
22 Piquancy (4)
25 Vacillated (7)
27 Lissome (5)
29 Expel from country (5)
30 Buffet restaurant (7)
31 Heron (5)
32 Lizard (5)

Down

2 Tales (5)
3 Supplication (7)
5 Donkeys (5)
6 Female avenger (7)
7 Church (5)
8 Semisolid food (5)
9 Pointer (5)
14 Spikes of corn (4)
16 Seep (4)
18 Raising (7)
20 On the loose (2,5)
21 Cricket shot (5)
23 Order (5)
24 Diary-writer (5)
26 Belgian city (5)
28 Modify slightly (5)

272

Across

1 *Trying to slow down* (7)
5 *Antelopes* (4)
7 Bishop's hat (5)
8 Simple life form (6)
10 Cattle (4)
11 Humiliated (8)
13 West wind (6)
14 Decorative gilt alloy (6)
17 Completely (8)
19 Leave (4)
21 Blank edge (6)
22 Motif (5)
23 Deliberately avoid (4)
24 Home ground (7)

Down

1 Deceived (10)
2 Belgian port (7)
3 Thing in list (4)
4 Rocky fragments (6)
5 Branch of mathematics (8)
6 Of town or city (5)
9 Adaptation (10)
12 Gaseous element (8)
15 Sumptuous (7)
16 Cringe (6)
18 Instruct (5)
20 Attempt (4)

273

Across

1 *Soothing ointment* (5)
4 *Loved dearly* (6)
8 *Former boxer* (3)
9 Lucky item? (9)
10 Policeman's traditional weapon (9)
12 Marsupial (inf.) (3)
13 Fish eggs (3)
14 Lightweight timber (5)
15 Rubbish (3)
16 Supporting structure (3)
18 Building by entrance (9)
20 Top US colleges (3,6)
22 Great dread (3)
23 Horse-drawn vehicle (6)
24 Top celebrities (1-4)

Down

1 Dippy type (12)
2 Spare time (7)
3 Moral code (5)
4 Melody (3)
5 Pacific region (7)
6 An anaesthetic (5)
7 Unsporting (5,3,4)
11 Israeli resort (5)
14 Particular irritation (7)
15 Tidal wave (7)
17 Watery area (US) (5)
19 African carnivore (5)
21 Chap (3)

274

Across

1 *Grasp, realise (slang)* (4)
4 *Enclosures* (4)
8 *Replete* (4)
9 Maid of Orleans (4,2,3)
11 Whirlpool (6)
13 Zincite (anag.) (7)
15 Elementary particle (6)
16 Saying (6)
18 Male feline (6)
20 Go away (6)
22 PM who followed two Labour PMs (7)
23 Florentine family (6)
25 Possession (9)
26 – and kin (4)
27 Contract; intertwine (4)
28 Voracious fish (4)

Down

2 Atop (4)
3 Insult (anag.) (6)
4 Diving bird (6)
5 Gave courage to (6)
6 Citation (9)
7 Bend (4)
10 Evergreen tree (7)
12 Pimple (4)
13 Article for trade (9)
14 Smokable plant (7)
17 Mild (4)
19 SE Asian island (6)
20 Deprived (6)
21 Chitchat (6)
23 Construct (4)
24 Pale red (4)

275

Across

1 *Chessman* (6)
4 *Town chief* (5)
8 Poor (5)
9 Unrestrained (7)
10 Performed (7)
11 Biting insect (4)
12 Epoch (3)
14 Of the ear (4)
15 Taunt (4)
18 Barrel (3)
21 From a distance (4)
23 Lethargic (7)
25 Upset, confuse (7)
26 Culpability (5)
27 Garb (5)
28 Erase (6)

Down

1 Doghouse (6)
2 Not correct (7)
3 Pile of cut grass (8)
4 Copy, ape (4)
5 Ache, crave (5)
6 Gyrate (6)
7 Raw, immature (5)
13 Pliant (8)
16 Bravery (7)
17 Frank, honest (6)
19 Orb (5)
20 Stick (6)
22 Passageway (5)
24 Ado (4)

276

Across

1 *Counterfeiter* (6)
4 *Examine* (5)
8 Weightless; lamp (5)
9 Cast aside (7)
10 Canadian province (7)
11 Release (4)
12 Young animal (3)
14 Autumn; drop (4)
15 Wander (4)
18 Root vegetable (3)
21 Sphere; dance (4)
23 Upshot (7)
25 Perpetual (7)
26 Kingdom (5)
27 Larceny (5)
28 Advise (6)

Down

1 Bird of prey (6)
2 Boat races (7)
3 Wholly (8)
4 Cajole (4)
5 Senior (5)
6 Doghouse (6)
7 Devastation (5)
13 Brotherhood (8)
16 Alligator pear (7)
17 Away (6)
19 American deer (5)
20 E.g. unpleasant rodents (6)
22 Large spoon (5)
24 Achievement (4)

277

Across

1 *Sprain* (5)
4 *Beach; prop (up)* (5)
8 Sea creature (7)
9 Sufficient (5)
10 Pleasure (13)
11 Blueprint (6)
12 Workshop (6)
15 Not conforming to the rules of syntax (13)
18 Passenger ship (5)
19 Fit of temper (7)
20 Antagonist (5)
21 Fire-raising (5)

Down

1 Incorrect (5)
2 Obstinacy (13)
3 Author of Kim (7)
4 A finch (6)
5 Japanese port, on Honshu (5)
6 Team spirit (6,2,5)
7 Shed (4-2)
11 Lookalike (6)
13 Queen of the fairies (7)
14 Blacksmith's forge (6)
16 Concur (5)
17 Citrus fruit (5)

278

Across

- **1** *Bellowed* (6)
- **5** *Snakelike fish* (4)
- **8** Appear (4)
- **9** Water channel (8)
- **10** Benefactor (6)
- **11** Moral excellence (6)
- **12** Delightful (11)
- **15** Fisherman (6)
- **17** Complete failure (6)
- **19** Nobleman (8)
- **20** Parched (4)
- **21** Guide; graphite (4)
- **22** Rugby player (6)

Down

- **2** Musical drama (5)
- **3** Ruefulness (7)
- **4** Fiend (5)
- **5** Mistake (5)
- **6** Lesson; reprimand (7)
- **7** Intelligent (6)
- **12** Thoughtful (7)
- **13** Vegetable (6)
- **14** Boastful threatening (7)
- **16** Easily understood (5)
- **17** Bring (5)
- **18** Lawbreaking (5)

The Telegraph

279

Across

1 *Fight (of honour)* (4)
3 *Insects* (4)
9 *Grey with age* (5)
10 Go with (9)
11 Observed (5)
12 Look back (9)
15 Opening in gun (6)
17 Numb (6)
19 Listless (9)
21 Admission (5)
23 Metallic element (9)
24 Dangers (5)
25 Eject (4)
26 Intend (4)

Down

1 A rant (8)
2 Burden (8)
4 Pass by (time) (6)
5 Timidity (7)
6 Enormous (4)
7 Stained (4)
8 Sign (4)
13 Kindle again (2-6)
14 Sample (8)
16 W. Indies music (7)
18 Standing (6)
20 Church recess (4)
21 Merit (4)
22 Undertaking (4)

280

Across

1 *Lingerie* (6)
4 *Renter* (5)
8 *Male whales* (5)
9 Protracted (7)
10 African republic (7)
11 Lake (4)
12 Large deer (3)
14 Astound (4)
15 Part of eye (4)
18 Deity (3)
21 Turf out (4)
23 Thorough (2-5)
25 Venetian boat (7)
26 Conjure up (5)
27 Attire (5)
28 Facet (6)

Down

1 Refined (6)
2 Joy (7)
3 Making certain (8)
4 Female deer (4)
5 Proportion (5)
6 Beat; tempo (6)
7 Aquatic growths (5)
13 Generosity (8)
16 Ameliorate (7)
17 Determined (6)
19 Couch (5)
20 Menace (6)
22 Logic (5)
24 Pigs (4)

281

Across

1 *Fleece* (4)
3 *Grim* (4)
6 *Possess* (3)
9 Clumsy (7)
10 Expression (5)
11 Wireless (5)
12 Breathtaking (7)
13 Meagre (6)
15 Emergency (6)
18 Unpaid (7)
20 Less (5)
23 Fire (5)
24 Obsequious (7)
25 Lament (3)
26 Haze (4)
27 Crooked (4)

Down

1 Seat (5)
2 Demanded (5)
4 Torment (6)
5 Elevate (5)
6 Menacing (7)
7 Figures (7)
8 Frolic (6)
13 Drool (7)
14 Mediocre (7)
16 Comment (6)
17 Against (6)
19 Reverie (5)
21 Innocent (5)
22 Fragrance (5)

282

Across

1 *One who complains* (6)
4 *Lessee* (6)
9 Occasions (5)
10 Perusal (7)
11 Age (3)
12 Tiny (5)
13 More rowdy (7)
15 Armpits echo (anag.) (11)
19 Less clear (7)
20 Alert (5)
21 Breakfast food (3)
22 A sitting (7)
24 Goes out (5)
25 Affectionate (6)
26 Remains in force (6)

Down

1 Unassuming (6)
2 Drawn (9)
3 Picture support (5)
5 Look into (7)
6 Winter sport accessory (3)
7 Look (6)
8 See-through (11)
14 Copy (9)
16 View (7)
17 Entertained (6)
18 Tightens up (6)
20 Spy (5)
23 Series (3)

The Telegraph

283

Across

1 *Nails* (5)
4 *Twosome* (4)
8 Flowering plant (7)
9 Saying (5)
10 Jockey (5)
11 Bland (7)
13 Operatic tenor (6)
15 Ancient country (6)
17 Bodily region (7)
20 Sound of sheep (5)
22 King of England (5)
23 Gets by coercion (7)
24 Strip skin off (4)
25 Herb (5)

Down

1 Nocturnal mammal (5)
2 Young genius (5,7)
3 Equal-sided rectangles (7)
4 Shopping centre (5)
5 American state (5)
6 Nine-day queen (4,4,4)
7 Venerate (6)
12 Hard fruit (3)
13 Cajoled (6)
14 Be in debt (3)
16 Natural environment (7)
18 Story's significance (5)
19 Impoverished (5)
21 Sample (5)

284

Across

1 *Move as liquid* (4)
3 *Steering lever* (6)
9 Derbyshire town (7)
10 Understood (5)
11 Bit of cloth (3)
12 Square dance (9)
13 Outlaw (6)
14 Vertical dimension (6)
16 Unlike Job (9)
19 Clothes fastener (3)
21 God of love (5)
22 University official (7)
23 Sell abroad (6)
24 Tax (4)

Down

1 Bone in leg (5)
2 Eight-sided figure (7)
4 Exclamation (12)
5 In nearby area (5)
6 Withdrawal (7)
7 Spanish imperialist (12)
8 Gull-like bird (4)
13 Soft roll (7)
15 Official journal (7)
17 Having jumping pages (3-2)
18 Catch sight of (4)
20 Celebration (5)

The Telegraph

285

Across

1 *London park* (4)
4 *Dingle* (4)
8 *Bad habit* (4)
9 Sandworms (anag.) (9)
11 GP (6)
13 Manipulated (7)
15 Hooter (6)
16 Bellowed (6)
18 Decimal (6)
20 Brusque (6)
22 Identity label (4,3)
23 Celestial body (6)
25 Sea monster (9)
26 Mountain goat (4)
27 Said (4)
28 Welsh resort (4)

Down

2 Gape (4)
3 Cerumen (6)
4 Singed (anag.) (6)
5 Chief (6)
6 Jazz dance (9)
7 Dread (4)
10 To be sure (2,5)
12 Read cursorily (4)
13 Lake District lake (4,5)
14 In name only (7)
17 Facts (4)
19 Job (6)
20 Antenna (6)
21 Bird of prey (6)
23 Cease (4)
24 Clownish (4)

The Telegraph

286

Across

1 *Eastern county* (7)
5 *Rowing crew* (5)
8 Single (5)
9 Lady's bedroom (7)
10 Meat dish (9)
12 Lie in sun (3)
13 Small pool (6)
14 Rather frightening (6)
17 Large cask (3)
18 Written notes (9)
20 Weapons store (7)
21 Cavalry sword (5)
23 Andean animal (5)
24 Tropical disease (7)

Down

1 Extinguish (candle) (5)
2 Not many (3)
3 Eccentric character (7)
4 Put a stop to; Sky HBO (anag.) (6)
5 Give out (5)
6 Deserted settlement (5,4)
7 Despotic rule (7)
11 Asian country (9)
13 Unexpected danger (7)
15 Sunshade (7)
16 Badge (6)
18 Heavenly food (5)
19 Cub leader (5)
22 Lawyers; pub (3)

287

Across

1 *Heart of a nut* (6)
4 *Four-wheeled truck* (5)
8 Indian currency (5)
9 Resolute (7)
10 Marine natural disaster (7)
11 Heavenly body (4)
12 Lair; study (3)
14 Nil (4)
15 Elliptical (4)
18 Regret (3)
21 Wreck (4)
23 Caller (7)
25 Changed (7)
26 Female relative (5)
27 In good time (5)
28 Jumper (6)

Down

1 Martial art (6)
2 Ecstasy (7)
3 Lift (8)
4 Prejudice (4)
5 Bestow; bursary (5)
6 Whole (6)
7 Swift (5)
13 Rubbish (8)
16 Naive (7)
17 Invent (6)
19 Elude (5)
20 Blood vessel (6)
22 Bury (5)
24 Quarry (4)

The Telegraph

288

Across

1 *Whimper* (5)
4 *Hungarian composer/ pianist* (5)
10 Lend money (7)
11 Nation (5)
12 Showy spring flower (5)
13 Daunting (7)
15 Lazy (4)
17 Dried plum (5)
19 Lever (5)
22 Male singer (4)
25 Ascetic (7)
27 Pig meat; essayist (5)
29 In good time (5)
30 Go before (7)
31 Quay (5)
32 Slender girl (5)

Down

2 Shack (5)
3 Skittle (7)
5 Edition; offspring (5)
6 Ardent (7)
7 Planet (5)
8 Lawful (5)
9 Gem (5)
14 Cried (4)
16 Expensive (4)
18 Save, book (7)
20 Stealing (7)
21 Humped animal (5)
23 Jumped (5)
24 Ire (5)
26 North African country (5)
28 Inexpensive (5)

The Telegraph

289

Across

1 *Fingerprint circles* (6)
5 *Delightful surprise* (5)
9 Put off (9)
10 Self-esteem (3)
11 Organ of sight (3)
12 International language (9)
14 Female rabbit (3)
16 Precise (5)
18 Limb (3)
19 Vegetable (9)
21 Weep (3)
22 Falsehood (3)
23 Bad dream (9)
25 Reside (5)
26 Avaricious (6)

Down

2 Speed (5)
3 Filled (7)
4 Transgression (3)
5 Royal house (5)
6 Everlasting (7)
7 Pedigree (12)
8 Stretched out completely (6-6)
13 Musical instrument (5)
15 Severe (7)
17 Playhouse (7)
20 Waterway (5)
21 Get to one's feet (5)
24 Carriage (3)

The Telegraph

290

Across

4 *Easy gallop* (6)
5 *Oval shape* (4)
7 Liberality (7)
10 Ward off (5)
11 Earn (7)
12 Plant with edible bulb (5)
14 Behaviour (7)
15 Phrygian king (5)
16 Italian composer (7)
20 Unspoken (5)
21 Recently born child (7)
22 Challenge (4)
23 Provide (6)

Down

1 Massage with hands (5)
2 Romantic poet (5)
3 Building for nuns (7)
4 Irish city (4)
6 Forgive (6)
8 Money in bank (7)
9 Boss (7)
10 Pear-shaped fruit (7)
13 Sorcerer (6)
14 Roe of sturgeon (7)
17 Arboreal primate (5)
18 Clumsy (5)
19 Remain (4)

The Telegraph

291

Across

1 *How come?* (3)
3 *Disposed of* (4)
5 *Wail* (4)
8 Annoy (8)
10 Shock (4)
11 Needle (3)
13 Itinerary (5)
14 Sum total (9)
16 Fellow (3)
17 Understand (3)
19 Ill-used (9)
21 Incendiarism (5)
22 Pose (3)
24 Redact (4)
25 Faker (8)
26 Roman garb (4)
27 Slips up (4)
28 Plan (3)

Down

1 Flog (4)
2 Thread (4)
3 Payment; village (10)
4 Baltic state (6)
6 Flare-up (8)
7 Tarried (8)
9 A Beatle (5)
12 Developing early (10)
14 Alongside (8)
15 Grinding (8)
18 Spooky (5)
20 Undercoat (6)
22 Stalk (4)
23 Snare (4)

The Telegraph

292

Across

1 *Fires* (5)
4 *Idiot* (3)
6 *Personal* (3)
8 Assorted (13)
9 Genuflect (5)
11 Cans (4)
13 Agile (5)
14 Late (5)
15 River outlet (5)
16 Front of ship (4)
18 Passive, immobile (5)
21 Disobedient (13)
23 Fool (3)
24 Look at (3)
25 Result, follow (5)

Down

1 Peak (6)
2 Barrel (4)
3 Creep (5)
4 Lubricate (3)
5 At last (7)
6 It measures distance travelled (8)
7 Snuggle (6)
10 Eagle's nest (5)
12 Obsession (8)
14 Sewer's aid (7)
15 Airman (anag) (6)
17 A good trick (6)
19 Nonsense (5)
20 Crowns (4)
22 Regret (3)

293

Across

1 *Tavern* (3)
3 *Small spot* (5)
6 *Hill* (3)
8 *County town of East Sussex* (5)
9 Status (7)
10 Arctic transport (10)
12 Attention; an organ (3)
15 Eye greedily (4)
17 Order (4)
18 Lair (3)
22 Discuss informally (4,6)
25 Muffin (7)
26 Bantu tribe (5)
27 Bric-a-brac (3)
28 Bucolic (5)
29 Dawdle (3)

Down

1 Mirage (8)
2 America (3,5)
3 Oil-producing plant (6)
4 Clothe (6)
5 Inflame (6)
6 Threesome (4)
7 Mania (4)
11 Consume (3)
13 Negation (8)
14 Exterior covering (8)
16 Expression of mild fright (3)
19 Small boy (6)
20 Winter sports participant (6)
21 Inhuman (6)
23 Shoo! (4)
24 Sect (4)

294

Across

1 *Motor* (3)
3 *Wait* (4)
5 *Charge* (4)
8 Complete (8)
10 Bucket (4)
11 Dram (3)
13 Reservoirs (5)
14 Cleanser (9)
16 Bustle (3)
17 Perceive (3)
19 Estranged (9)
21 Volumes (5)
22 Pose (3)
24 Margin (4)
25 Mandibles (8)
26 Benevolent (4)
27 Bazaar (4)
28 Hostelry (3)

Down

1 Natter (4)
2 Surplus (4)
3 Twaddle (10)
4 Senility (6)
6 Scaremonger (8)
7 Recruited (8)
9 Uninterested (5)
12 Apparent (10)
14 Dawn (8)
15 Sledge (8)
18 Weird (5)
20 Unhinged (6)
22 Rebuff (4)
23 Emperor (4)

The Telegraph

295

Across

1 *Funeral car* (6)
4 *Owl's call* (4)
8 Power to entice (6)
9 Slumbering (6)
10 Put forward (5)
11 Bunch of flowers (7)
13 Cattle (4)
15 Curve (3)
16 US university (4)
18 Preliminary exercises (4-3)
20 Garden tool (5)
23 Rodent (6)
24 Unimportant things (6)
25 Hard wood (4)
26 Bandage (6)

Down

1 Minster town (7)
2 Sharp (5)
3 Canal location (4)
5 Opprobrium (7)
6 Subject (5)
7 Holiday island (7)
12 Whig statesman (7)
14 African republic (7)
17 Opponent of progress (7)
19 Representative (5)
21 Copy of painting (5)
22 Pack (4)

296

Across

1 *Sorrowing* (8)
7 *Beatle Ringo* (5)
8 Differently (9)
9 Donkey (3)
10 Anticipation (4)
11 Wine room? (6)
13 Sea journey (6)
14 Alter (6)
17 Bird of prey (6)
18 Cleansing agent (4)
20 Owed (3)
22 Planner (9)
23 Foolish (5)
24 Outside (8)

Down

1 Skulk (5)
2 Sad (7)
3 Typical standard (4)
4 Fixed (6)
5 Arab peninsula (5)
6 Cut of meat (7)
7 Shut off (7)
12 Nimbleness (7)
13 Bridge (7)
15 Ideal (7)
16 Tail bone (6)
17 Savage (5)
19 Group of interviewers (5)
21 V (4)

297

Across

1 *Watery city* (6)
4 *Captain Ahab, e.g.* (6)
7 Very tall (8)
9 Mythological patricide (7)
12 Heat unit (5)
13 London Mayor (5)
15 Jewish leader (5)
16 Little orphan girl (5)
17 Shakespearean forest (5)
18 Evil spirit (5)
19 Quack cure (7)
23 From a geographical area (8)
24 Large nut (6)
25 Rather cold (6)

Down

1 Herbivorous person (10)
2 Those who don't belong (3-7)
3 New York university (8)
4 Reward for work (4)
5 Sparkling wine (4)
6 Jacob's brother (4)
8 Paris cathedral (5-4)
10 Amazing (10)
11 Film script (10)
14 Picnic food (8)
20 Finished (4)
21 Confused state (4)
22 Russian river (4)

The Telegraph

298

Across

1 *Caper* (5)
4 *Citrus fruit* (4)
8 *Cut down* (3)
9 Restaurant (9)
10 Fable (4)
11 Woman in Roman legend (8)
12 Hat (3)
13 Hummable (6)
14 That's delicious! (3-3)
16 — Dawson, comedian (3)
17 Set point (anag.) (4,2,2)
18 Smile (4)
20 Walk with help of free rides (5-4)
21 Duo (3)
22 Toy (2-2)
23 Canoe (5)

Down

1 Pale (7)
2 Of vision, normal (6-6)
3 Famous clown (4)
4 Encourage (4,2)
5 Passenger vehicle (5,3)
6 Knick-knack; over-dainty (6-6)
7 Hidden ditch (2-2)
11 Non-clerical (3)
12 Child's word for train (4-4)
14 Nevertheless (3)
15 Males (7)
16 Instinctive desire (6)
17 London district (4)
19 Stream (4)

The Telegraph

299

Across

1 *Name for a parrot* (5)
3 *Venetian painter* (6)
7 Ewes' milk cheese (9)
9 Encounter (4)
10 Near (4)
11 Ire (5)
13 Prize (6)
14 Eagle's nest (5)
15 Lucid; to empty (5)
17 Trader (6)
20 Dissuade (5)
21 Staff; spice (4)
23 Particle (4)
24 Loquacious (9)
25 Purloined (6)
26 Of the city (5)

Down

1 Allow (6)
2 Booty (4)
3 Chewy confection (6)
4 Ripped (4)
5 Darkness (5)
6 Comical (5)
7 Remember (9)
8 Tease (9)
11 In front (5)
12 – Cup, biennial golf tournament (5)
16 Calculate (6)
17 Demise (5)
18 Stay (6)
19 Accumulate (5)
22 A peer (4)
23 Assert (4)

300

Across

1 *Worktop* (7)
5 *Deed* (4)
7 Unadorned (5)
8 Floral cotton cloth (6)
10 Droplet; rip (4)
11 Torpor (8)
13 Ogled (6)
14 Summer month (6)
17 Ragged (8)
19 Blemish (4)
21 Vocation; rush (6)
22 Dogma (5)
23 Workshy (4)
24 Shoulder bone (7)

Down

1 Surrender (10)
2 Ignorant (7)
3 Minute (4)
4 Clamour (6)
5 Loyal (8)
6 Change (5)
9 Enigmatic (10)
12 Graveyard (8)
15 Indistinct (7)
16 Hunt (6)
18 Headdress (5)
20 Swindle (4)

The Telegraph

301

Across

1 *Express pleasure* (4)
5 *Recognise* (4)
7 Stick out unpleasantly (7)
8 US composer (8)
10 Ceremonial splendour (4)
12 Breeding stable (4)
14 Know-all (8)
16 Agent of change (8)
17 Sewing case (4)
18 Story of gods (4)
19 Sample (8)
22 Bland (7)
23 Persistent strife (4)
24 Church recess (4)

Down

1 Piece of publicity (4)
2 Diana —, Motown singer (4)
3 Person hiding on ship (8)
4 Destroy (4)
5 Memento (8)
6 Strike with strap (4)
9 Sea inlet (7)
11 Large tent (7)
13 Trim faded bloom (4-4)
15 Famous auction house (8)
18 Annoy (4)
19 Dull (4)
20 Notion (4)
21 Main part of church (4)

302

Across

1 *Sandbank* (4)
4 *Be king* (5)
8 Loss of appetite (8)
9 & 20 Herman Melville novel (4-4)
10 Teem (4)
11 Aide-mémoire (8)
12 Allow (6)
14 Detective (6)
16 Amiable (8)
19 Casserole (4)
20 *See 9 Across*
21 Adulthood (8)
22 Go in (5)
23 Ceremony (4)

Down

2 Mistake (5)
3 Ballroom dance (7)
4 Kingdom (5)
5 Vast (7)
6 Aristocratic (5)
7 Revenue (6)
13 Mongoose-like animal (7)
14 Unethical lawyer (7)
15 Pact (6)
17 Lift (5)
18 Disagree (5)
19 Swagger (5)

The Telegraph

303

Across

1 *Bloodsucker* (4)
3 *Rip* (4)
6 *Limb* (3)
9 Conclusively (4,3,3,3)
10 Plastic money (4,4)
12 Siamese (4)
13 Spike of corn (3)
15 Computer (6)
18 Religious founder (6)
19 Fresh (3)
21 Skin (4)
22 Wall scrawls! (8)
25 Musical arrangement (13)
26 Unhappy (3)
27 Uncommon (4)
28 Spoken (4)

Down

1 Soccer gambling (8,5)
2 Old lag (2-3)
4 Stand (6)
5 Bird; castle (4)
6 Self-conscious (7)
7 Large company (13)
8 Kingfisher (7)
11 Flatfish (3)
14 Thug (7)
16 Punctured (7)
17 Wooden pin (3)
20 Author (6)
23 Colder (5)
24 Large animal (4)

SOLUTIONS

The Telegraph

Solutions 1–2

1

Across:
1 Poll
4 Sap
6 Art (Poles apart)
8 Manufacturer
10 Cringe
12 Cinema
13 Ebbed
14 Aunt
15 Crib
17 Under
19 Injury
21 Danger
23 Nursery rhyme
24 Lay
25 Tun
26 Rank

Down:
2 Oration
3 Lounge
4 Slay
5 Putrid
6 Agree
7 Threadbare
9 Occasional
11 Ebony
12 Ceded
16 Regimen
17 Urgent
18 Rasher
20 Jerky
22 Hymn

2

Across:
1 Spar
5 City (Sparsity)
7 Awesome
8 Adhesive
10 Evil
12 Tsar
14 Nonsense
16 Carefree
17 Year
18 Idol
19 Tolerate
22 Nemesis
23 Agog
24 Else

Down:
1 Sofa
2 Race
3 Beginner
4 Lose
5 Cemetery
6 Yell
9 Discard
11 Instant
13 Riesling
15 Needless
18 Idea
19 Tomb
20 Ruse
21 Edge

Solutions 3–4

3

Across:

1	Trance
5	Later (Translator)
9	Underhand
10	Tim
11	Tin
12	Agamemnon
14	Rig
16	Aspic
18	Sir
19	Crescendo
21	Bet
22	Tea
23	Armadillo
25	Heavy
26	Durham

Down:

2	Rodin
3	Nirvana
4	Era
5	Lodge
6	Tetanus
7	Remuneration
8	Butterscotch
13	Aspen
15	Grenada
17	Chowder
20	Chary
21	Balsa
24	Mad

4

Across:

1	Bell
5	Ease (Belize)
7	Albumen
8	McCarthy
10	Item
12	Wood
14	Chop-chop
16	Judgment
17	Ezra
18	Stab
19	Trollope
22	Disband
23	Tiny
24	Yoga

Down:

1	Balm
2	Lava
3	Obstacle
4	Emmy
5	Encircle
6	Edam
9	Croquet
11	Ego-trip
13	Dogsbody
15	Optional
18	Sift
19	Task
20	Lady
21	Elba

Solutions 5–6

5

Across:
1 Hair
4 Deed
8 Daze (Heady days)
9 Patriarch
11 Eyelet
13 Alleged
15 Kenyan
16 Driver
18 Arouse
20 Stanza
22 Unguent
23 Italic
25 Tolerable
26 Itch
27 Kerb
28 Sump

Down:
2 Alas
3 Rarely
4 Deaden
5 Exceed
6 Gallivant
7 Lent
10 Hydrate
12 Skua
13 Annoyance
14 Lawsuit
17 Roam
19 Encode
20 Superb
21 Annals
23 Iris
24 Slim

6

Across:
1 Spies
4 Curls (Spice Girls)
10 Gelatin
11 Audio
12 Tease
13 Ejected
15 Afro
17 Bantu
19 Wheel
22 Solo
25 Usurped
27 Macho
29 Oaths
30 Upgrade
31 Acted
32 V-sign

Down:
2 Polka
3 Entreat
5 Usage
6 Ladette
7 Agate
8 Anger
9 Wordy
14 Jowl
16 Fuse
18 Aquatic
20 Homages
21 Buxom
23 Odium
24 Dozes
26 Paste
28 Clang

Solutions 7–8

7

Across:
- **1** Gore
- **4** Gone
- **8** Zola (Gorgonzola)
- **9** Camembert
- **11** Damson
- **13** Spheric
- **15** Potter
- **16** Cinema
- **18** Retort
- **20** Fleece
- **22** Doe-eyed
- **23** Hyssop
- **25** Mongooses
- **26** Lair
- **27** Stye
- **28** Ewer

Down:
- **2** Okay
- **3** Exempt
- **4** Gibber
- **5** Nordic
- **6** Bolstered
- **7** Yarn
- **10** Tacitly
- **12** Spar
- **13** Statistic
- **14** Heirdom
- **17** Apex
- **19** Top out
- **20** Fergie
- **21** Eeyore
- **23** Hold
- **24** Fete

8

Across:
- **1** Honour
- **4** None (On and on)
- **8** Jovial
- **9** Before
- **10** Alter
- **11** Citadel
- **13** Smug
- **15** Tag
- **16** Dark
- **18** Dignity
- **20** Rowdy
- **23** Effect
- **24** Abduct
- **25** Rile
- **26** Spiral

Down:
- **1** Hoodlum
- **2** Naive
- **3** Ugly
- **5** Offhand
- **6** Eerie
- **7** Abridge
- **12** Statute
- **14** Genteel
- **17** Radical
- **19** Infer
- **21** Order
- **22** Damp

Solutions 9–10

9

Across:

1 Cue
3 Tickle (Cuticle)
7 Arizona
8 Welsh
10 Deft
11 Meerkats
13 Barque
15 Player
17 Lyricist
18 Memo
21 Rabbi
22 Ravioli
23 Stingy
24 Dry

Down:

1 Chief
2 Eros
3 Travel
4 Cowardly
5 Lullaby
6 Mandibular
9 Histrionic
12 Junction
14 Rarebit
16 Osprey
19 Epoxy
20 Ovid

10

Across:

1 Beau
4 Charred (Boatyard)
8 Conjugal
9 Nap
11 Queasy
13 Kruger
14 Tonne
15 Awry
17 Deem
18 Stuff
20 Attach
21 Eleven
24 Ice
25 Trappist
26 Extreme
27 York

Down:

2 Evoke
3 Unjust
4 Cage
5 Allure
6 Renegue
7 Deportment
10 Aquamarine
12 Youth
13 Knife
16 Retreat
18 Scythe
19 Floppy
22 Visor
23 Haze

Solutions 11–12

11

Across:

1 Moscow
4 Munich
9 Asian (Mass communication)
10 Lectern
11 Eel
12 Mused
13 Unicorn
15 Marchioness
19 Gremlin
20 Blaze
21 Ire
22 Tetanus
24 Bigot
25 Arable
26 Apathy

Down:

1 Miasma
2 Shipshape
3 Owned
5 Unction
6 Ice
7 Honing
8 Illusionist
14 Onslaught
16 Colonel
17 Agatha
18 Vestry
20 Bebop
23 Tea

12

Across:

1 Inn
3 Dee
5 Pend
7 Dense (Independence)
8 Day-old
10 Copy
11 Insignia
13 Senile
14 Damask
17 Vacation
19 Frau
21 Appear
22 Robot
23 Envy
24 Ham
25 Try

Down:

1 Indecisive
2 Ninepin
3 Diet
4 Ending
5 Physical
6 Nylon
9 Bankruptcy
12 Flattery
15 Acrobat
16 Fourth
18 Capon
20 Brim

Solutions 13–14

13

Across:

1 Sir
3 Kit
5 Bored (Circuit board)
8 Ulcer
9 Beijing
10 Deaf
11 Penzance
13 Gideon
14 Graves
17 Assemble
19 Onus
22 Uniform
23 Royal
24 Liked
25 Sex
26 Ewe

Down:

1 Squad
2 Richard
3 Kirk
4 Tablet
5 Blizzard
6 Reign
7 Digress
12 Wormwood
13 Gradual
15 Vandyke
16 Glamis
18 Stick
20 Solve
21 Crux

14

Across:

1 Crew
4 Sibyl (Crucible)
8 Accurate
9 Lead
10 Sued
11 Happened
12 Stupor
14 Rueful
16 Accident
19 Also
20 Tact
21 Gangster
22 Error
23 Eden

Down:

2 Round
3 Weather
4 Sleep
5 Believe
6 Leave
7 Acquit
13 Painter
14 Retinue
15 Ulster
17 Chase
18 Eager
19 Aisle

Solutions 15–16

15

Across:

1 Diner
4 Sore (Dinosaur)
7 Omit
8 Vehement
9 Encounter
10 Spy
12 Scrape
14 Tarzan
16 Owe
18 Querulous
21 Sidestep
22 Foil
23 Stir
24 Niche

Down:

1 Demonic
2 Notional
3 Raven
4 Sumo
5 Run-up
6 Threat
11 Prolific
13 Equity
15 Abusive
17 Wrist
19 Ripen
20 Jeer

16

Across:

1 Coal
3 Chaired (Cultured)
8 Bureau
9 Touchy
10 Separate
11 Ebbs
12 Ascend
15 Shifty
17 Flag
19 Salivate
22 Fibula
23 Daring
24 Isolate
25 Mean

Down:

1 Crude
2 Average
4 Hatters
5 Inure
6 Exhibit
7 Puma
13 Sallies
14 Distant
16 Inverse
18 Gruel
20 Lads
21 Tenon

Solutions 17–18

17

Across:
1 Annas
4 Teak
8 Off (A nasty cough)
9 Fireplace
10 Foxy
11 Admonish
12 Use
13 Yodels
14 Feints
16 Bid
17 Publican
18 Blot
20 Mediators
21 Air
22 Keen
23 Ankle

Down:
1 Aloofly
2 No fixed abode
3 Safe
4 Tirade
5 Approved
6 National park
7 Mesh
11 Ass
12 Ultimate
14 Fin
15 Set free
16 Baboon
17 Pomp
19 Asia

18

Across:
1 Prints
5 Char
8 Ming (Prince Charming)
9 Intruder
10 Invert
11 Impair
12 Get-together
15 Adroit
17 Dabble
19 Strimmer
20 Tote
21 Ghee
22 Esteem

Down:
2 Reign
3 Neglect
4 Skint
5 Chump
6 Atelier
7 Attire
12 Go Dutch
13 On time
14 Habitat
16 Opine
17 Dirge
18 Lithe

Solutions 19–20

19

Across:
1 Hut
3 Haste
6 Err
8 Funny (A Taste of Honey)
9 Repress
10 Imitations
12 Dog
15 Sell
17 Wrap
18 Eat
22 Proprietor
25 Cleanse
26 Unfit
27 Dot
28 Horse
29 Lad

Down:
1 Heftiest
2 Tangible
3 Heyday
4 Sordid
5 Expand
6 Eden
7 Risk
11 Sow
13 Grateful
14 Spirited
16 Lap
19 Trench
20 Appear
21 Minute
23 Acid
24 Bent

20

Across:
1 Beast
4 Herd (Bestirred)
8 Bequest
9 Amour
10 Llama
11 Satisfy
13 Vanish
15 Candid
17 Analogy
20 Gauze
22 Lucre
23 Worktop
24 Pass
25 April

Down:
1 Babel
2 Acquaintance
3 The Oaks
4 Hates
5 Roast
6 Loss adjuster
7 Frayed
12 Arc
13 Viable
14 Hog
16 Algeria
18 Opera
19 Yawns
21 Expel

Solutions 21–22

21

Across:
- **1** Paris
- **4** Ending (Parascending)
- **9** Taffeta
- **10** Taste
- **11** Ibex
- **12** Jackpot
- **13** Zoo
- **14** Shoe
- **16** Soda
- **18** Wee
- **20** Lorelei
- **21** Tail
- **24** Quest
- **25** Console
- **26** Essays
- **27** Piety

Down:
- **1** Patois
- **2** Rifle
- **3** Stem
- **5** Notecase
- **6** Insipid
- **7** Ghetto
- **8** Banjo
- **13** Zealotry
- **15** Harness
- **17** Plaque
- **18** Winch
- **19** Sleepy
- **22** Above
- **23** Snip

22

Across:
- **1** Clique
- **4** Attic
- **8** Click (Clickety-click)
- **9** Ramekin
- **10** Dragnet
- **11** Snap
- **12** Hip
- **14** Fell
- **15** Hiss
- **18** Yam
- **21** Rusk
- **23** Aerosol
- **25** Tourism
- **26** Spear
- **27** Candy
- **28** Sexton

Down:
- **1** Cicada
- **2** Imitate
- **3** Unkindly
- **4** Army
- **5** Token
- **6** Canape
- **7** Broth
- **13** Pharisee
- **16** Suspect
- **17** Critic
- **19** Magma
- **20** Florin
- **22** Spurn
- **24** Wily

Solutions 23–24

23

Across:

1 Penal
5 Serve
8 Etude (Penal servitude)
9 Wring
10 Backfired
11 Sou
12 Predestined
15 Prickly pear
19 All
20 Copyright
22 Ingot
23 Apron
24 Totem
25 Gored

Down:

1 Pawnshop
2 Nail up
3 Leg break
4 Muscle
5 Self
6 Rat run
7 Eyed
13 Treating
14 Deflated
16 Impost
17 Yogurt
18 Ranger
20 Colt
21 Ream

24

Across:

1 Soup
3 Official (Superficial)
9 Annul
10 Refrain
11 Pie
13 Avalanche
14 Reason
16 Reuben
18 Propagate
20 Ewe
22 Oration
23 Sleep
25 Eternity
26 Eddy

Down:

1 Sharp
2 Urn
4 Formal
5 Inflame
6 Irascible
7 Lantern
8 Plea
12 Elaborate
14 Reprove
15 Ovation
17 Garnet
19 Easy
21 Empty
24 End

Solutions 25–26

25

Across:

1 Pique
3 Oxtail (Peacock's tail)
7 Beautiful
9 Deed
10 Till
11 Faint
13 Entail
14 Taper
15 Moult
17 Static
20 Dirty
21 Need
23 Anon
24 Nightmare
25 Excess
26 Eager

Down:

1 Pledge
2 Used
3 Orient
4 Taut
5 Ladle
6 Mural
7 Beethoven
8 Libertine
11 Field
12 Tasty
16 Tights
17 Stamp
18 Concur
19 Uncle
22 Dire
23 Aria

26

Across:

1 Pastor
4 Weigh (Passed away)
8 Above
9 Replied
10 Unaware
11 Ogre
12 Dip
14 Ghee
15 Oats
18 See
21 Each
23 Lorries
25 Shampoo
26 Dense
27 Woman
28 Learnt

Down:

1 Plague
2 Stomach
3 Operates
4 Wept
5 Icing
6 Hidden
7 Urged
13 Porridge
16 Thinner
17 Seesaw
19 Elbow
20 Aspect
22 Claim
24 Open

Solutions 27–28

27

Across:		Down:	
1	Fare	2	Ascot
4	Aisle (Fair Isle)	3	Eritrea
8	Mischief	4	Awful
9	Rare	5	Servant
10	Felt	6	Enrol
11	Reliable	7	Digest
12	Stigma	13	General
14	Detest	14	Duchess
16	Frenetic	15	Soccer
19	Luck	17	React
20	Fair	18	Tramp
21	Aberdeen	19	Lodge
22	Tulip		
23	Seem		

28

Across:		Down:	
1	Yukon	1	Yemen
4	Twin (You can't win)	2	Kindergarten
8	Menaces	3	Nucleus
9	Tacit	4	Taste
10	Niece	5	Inter
11	En route	6	Acquaintance
13	Ingest	7	Stress
15	Pupils	12	Nap
17	Corrupt	13	Income
20	Put up	14	Tap
22	Meets	16	Umpteen
23	Eternal	18	Upset
24	Stud	19	Tread
25	Needy	21	Pally

Solutions 29–30

29

Across:
1 Docked
4 Hearse
7 Hoarders (Doctor's orders)
9 Opposed
12 Motor
13 Scrub
15 Douse
16 Iraqi
17 Steer
19 Death
20 Yiddish
24 Hotelier
25 Sorrow
26 Rennet

Down:
1 Dehumidify
2 Coastguard
3 Endorses
4 Hasp
5 Also
6 Save
8 Roar
10 Separation
11 Disinherit
14 Bird's-eye
18 Echo
21 Into
22 Dear
23 Show

30

Across:
1 Isle
4 Beer
8 Bark (I'll be back)
9 Bedspread
11 Turgid
13 Leaflet
15 Credit
16 Disarm
18 Master
20 Qualms
22 Repulse
23 Carton
25 Notarised
26 Dull
27 Envy
28 Nude

Down:
2 Shed
3 Ensued
4 Bereft
5 Elated
6 Laughable
7 Skid
10 Dutiful
12 Scum
13 Leisurely
14 Aileron
17 Mist
19 Renown
20 Queasy
21 Assign
23 Code
24 Mend

Solutions 31–32

31

Across:

1 Indie
4 Nile (In denial)
7 Epic
8 Ignominy
9 Deceitful
10 Bed
12 Uses up
14 Harass
16 Opt
18 Rough-hewn
21 Wildfire
22 Book
23 Fens
24 Motif

Down:

1 Impress
2 Decrease
3 Exist
4 Name
5 Lance
6 Onrush
11 Prohibit
13 Phobia
15 Sawn-off
17 Poise
19 Gleam
20 Odds

32

Across:

7 Higher
8 Queues (I accuse … or High IQs)
10 Mahatma
11 Hegel
12 Esau
13 Edwin
17 Stalk
18 Shah
22 Hazel
23 Sixteen
24 Shrimp
25 Scheme

Down:

1 Whimper
2 Egghead
3 Jetty
4 Fuchsia
5 Budge
6 Psalm
9 Vandalism
14 Ptolemy
15 Thieves
16 Channel
19 Chasm
20 Azure
21 Exact

Solutions 33–34

33

Across:

1 Mill
3 Ascent (Millicent)
9 Remorse
10 Bevel
11 Two
12 Tennessee
13 Danube
14 Jumble
16 Eiderdown
19 Eel
21 Slain
22 Roll-top
23 Reflex
24 Zeal

Down:

1 Merit
2 Lampoon
4 Subsequently
5 Eaves
6 Toluene
7 Protuberance
8 Keen
13 Dresser
15 Breathe
17 Dwarf
18 Ogre
20 Lapel

34

Across:

1 Mull
4 Akin
8 Tire (Mull of Kintyre)
9 Slingshot
11 Nought
13 Meander
15 In a rut
16 Dotard
18 Gossip
20 Streak
22 Tabloid
23 Ballot
25 Red Planet
26 Club
27 Stop
28 Daft

Down:

2 Ugly
3 Linger
4 Assent
5 Ironed
6 Disgraced
7 Best
10 Toronto
12 Sing
13 Mausoleum
14 Auditor
17 Duke
19 Patent
20 Slip-up
21 Ribald
23 Back
24 Beef

Solutions 35–36

35

Across:

1 Yule
4 Lessees (Ulysses)
8 Scimitar
9 Ego
11 Rotund
13 Abbess
14 Eagle
15 Ibex
17 Star
18 Idiom
20 Clergy
21 Yeoman
24 Ion
25 Apostasy
26 Dullard
27 Rant

Down:

2 Uncut
3 Ermine
4 Loth
5 Scribe
6 Element
7 Shoestring
10 Brainchild
12 Dandy
13 Alloy
16 Eternal
18 Iguana
19 Mentor
22 Mason
23 Fold

36

Across:

7 Vile
8 Inn
9 Beau (Violin bow)
10 Shrimp
11 Laxity
12 Lie
13 Praise
14 Retort
16 Cygnet
19 Chance
21 Woo
22 Rabble
24 Rescue
25 Also
26 Tie
27 Each

Down:

1 Wither
2 Derision
3 Simple
4 Angler
5 Ibex
6 Banter
15 Transfer
17 Yearly
18 Twenty
19 Corset
20 Crutch
23 Blot

Solutions 37–38

37

Across:

1 Berth
4 Marque (Birthmark)
9 Tactful
10 Exact
11 Earn
12 Atheist
13 Par
14 Rave
16 Stye
18 Fit
20 Recover
21 Pail
24 Steer
25 Sapling
26 Rotter
27 Scent

Down:

1 Bitter
2 Recur
3 Haft
5 Amethyst
6 Quality
7 Estate
8 Clear
13 Perverse
15 Ancient
17 Eraser
18 Fresh
19 Alight
22 Agile
23 Opus

38

Across:

1 Stare
4 Welles (Stairwells)
7 Literal
8 Blow
10 Drake
11 Leather
14 Styx
16 Rotate
18 Impact
21 Alto
23 Trotsky
26 Angel
27 Mill
28 Eritrea
29 Inform
30 Gravy

Down:

1 Solidarity
2 Attract
3 Earnest
4 Wildly
5 Libra
6 Epoch
9 Fritillary
12 Exit
13 Top
15 Teak
17 Aft
19 Moaning
20 Algeria
22 Lyceum
24 Onion
25 Salvo

Solutions 39–40

39

Across:

1 Paw
3 Chew
5 Gull (Portugal)
8 Illusion
10 Stun
11 Rot
13 Ledge
14 Epaulette
16 Ayr
17 Too
19 Negligent
21 Isaac
22 Jet
24 Else
25 Marinate
26 Sash
27 Type
28 Ask

Down:

1 Pair
2 Wilt
3 Casablanca
4 Exocet
6 Up-to-date
7 Lancelot
9 Loopy
12 Plebiscite
14 Easiness
15 Arkansas
18 Onset
20 Galaxy
22 Java
23 Teak

40

Across:

1 Dare
4 Reef
8 Arms (Dairy farms)
9 Purchaser
11 Nodded
13 Frailty
15 Beetle
16 Saucer
18 Titles
20 Streak
22 Annoyed
23 Parade
25 Yesterday
26 Tone
27 Espy
28 Team

Down:

2 Abut
3 Escort
4 Roadie
5 Events
6 Predicted
7 Used
10 Royalty
12 Abet
13 Featuring
14 Already
17 Rake
19 Sneers
20 Softly
21 Regret
23 Pity
24 Data

Solutions 41–42

41

Across:

1 Mare
4 See
6 Bow
9 Coo (Merci beaucoup)
10 Rabbi
11 Staid
12 Uttermost
15 Fortune-teller
19 Greenhorn
21 Bluer
22 Acorn
24 Ice
25 Yes
26 Elf
27 Axel

Down:

2 Adopter
3 Error
4 Sob
5 Epistle
6 Bleak
7 Wild
8 Scruffy
13 Obese
14 Bronzed
16 Upgrade
17 Leonine
18 Quays
20 Ninja
21 Bevy
23 Oaf

42

Across:

1 Moor
4 Cherry (Mortuary)
7 Ado
9 Smug
10 Petanque
11 Gas
12 Ache
13 Earphone
16 Lady Bountiful
19 Identity
23 Iona
24 End
25 Jeroboam (or Rehoboam)
26 Ibis
27 Emu
28 Severn
29 Mime

Down:

2 Of Mice and Men
3 Raggedy
4 Copse
5 Enter
6 Ranch
8 Quinquennium
14 Adult
15 Pot
17 Bet
18 Iridium
20 Noose
21 In one
22 Yemen

Solutions 43–44

43

Across:
1 More
3 Good
9 Issue (Mogadishu)
10 Tasteless
11 Cadge
12 Resonance
15 Averse
17 Innate
19 Imitation
21 Habit
23 Temperate
24 Spite
25 Norm
26 Mess

Down:
1 Maternal
2 Resisted
4 Oceans
5 Discern
6 Used
7 Cede
8 Keen
13 Salivate
14 Meanness
16 Smitten
18 Simmer
20 Apex
21 Host
22 Bait

44

Across:
1 Adieu
4 Drop (A dewdrop)
8 Apparel
9 Louse
10 Masai
11 Tetanus
13 Arnhem
15 Breezy
17 Context
20 Caste
22 Visas
23 Intense
24 Myth
25 Leeds

Down:
1 Alarm
2 Imposingness
3 Ukraine
4 Delft
5 Owlet
6 Quintessence
7 Jersey
12 Ebb
13 Alcove
14 Mix
16 Recital
18 Essay
19 Thigh
21 Epees

Solutions 45–46

45

Across:

1 Maxim
4 Million (Maximilian)
8 Zen
9 Col
10 Abyss
11 Range
12 Bravery
15 True
17 Apathy
19 Adjust
22 Dome
24 Conquer
26 Bacon
28 Motif
30 Cos
31 Bye
32 Layette
33 Yeast

Down:

1 Mazurka
2 Xenon
3 Macbeth
4 Malibu
5 Llama
6 Ivy
7 Nasty
13 Ream
14 Emu
16 Ryde
18 Awn
20 Debussy
21 Tangent
23 Oracle
24 Camel
25 Unfit
27 Cobra
29 Try

46

Across:

1 Milk
4 Sheikh (Milkshake)
7 Nut
9 Stye
10 Outboard
11 Sir
12 Alms
13 King Kong
16 Leather jacket
19 Stone axe
23 Cast
24 Ark
25 Farthing
26 Pied
27 Lei
28 Chaste
29 Tank

Down:

2 Intellectual
3 Knesset
4 Stork
5 Eaten
6 Kiosk
8 Frankenstein
14 Ibrox
15 Goa
17 Hoe
18 Cockpit
20 Notch
21 Alias
22 Eagle

Solutions 47–48

47

Across:

1 Pant
4 Tea
6 Hoes (Pantyhose)
8 Upturn
9 Tumble
10 Tentacle
11 Nave
12 Underclothing
17 Scud
19 Bowsprit
22 Clever
23 Addict
24 Vest
25 Toy
26 Park

Down:

2 Ample
3 Trustee
4 Tonic
5 Art deco
6 Human
7 Enliven
10 Tau
13 Nacelle
14 Cabaret
15 Hyped up
16 Gut
18 Divot
20 Weary
21 Incur

48

Across:

1 Proper
4 Gander (Propaganda)
7 Dulcimer
9 Centaur
12 Sight
13 Inner
15 Ratio
16 Atlas
17 Nomad
18 Issue
19 Nonplus
23 Restless
24 Change
25 Orated

Down:

1 Pedestrian
2 Obligation
3 Eviction
4 Gore
5 Neat
6 Esau
8 Economise
10 Adolescent
11 Reassessed
14 Radiator
20 Oath
21 Plan
22 Urge

Solutions 49–50

49

Across:

1 Consent
8 Rating (Concentrating)
9 Started
11 Derelict
12 Fussy
14 Onus
15 Distrust
17 Emphatic
18 Veto
20 Laden
21 Generous
23 Stratum
24 Eleven
25 Epithet

Down:

2 Outrun
3 Stress
4 Need
5 Majesty
6 Ridiculed
7 Agitation
10 Delicious
12 Foreigner
13 Suspended
16 Married
18 Vacant
19 Tenure
22 Step

50

Across:

1 Queue
4 Brute (Cube root)
8 Appoint
9 Anger
10 Leisure centre
11 Sydney
12 Sprout
15 Encouragement
18 Paris
19 Everest
20 Sitar
21 Delay

Down:

1 Quail
2 Esprit de corps
3 Epicure
4 Butler
5 Usage
6 Eightsome reel
7 Urgent
11 Sleepy
13 Pretend
14 Career
16 Upset
17 Tatty

Solutions 51–52

51

Across:		Down:	
1	Boast	1	Blimp
4	Wring (Bowstring)	2	Advertisement
8	Invaded	3	Toddler
9	Lunch	4	Widget
10	Parallelogram	5	Igloo
11	Priory	6	Generalissimo
12	Dallas	7	Thames
15	Steeplechaser	11	Pisces
18	Event	13	Athlete
19	Preview	14	People
20	Thyme	16	Petty
21	Ebony	17	Rowdy

52

Across:		Down:	
1	Aura	1	Adam's apple
3	Terse (Orators)	2	Aniseed
7	Ibex	3	Twerps
8	Accidental	4	Rotate
9	Alto	5	Eilat
12	Sweet potato	6	Beat
13	Prado	10	Loft
15	Motor	11	Outrageous
19	Everlasting	14	Axed
21	Eddy	16	Outward
23	Impresario	17	Drop in
24	Bran	18	Camera
25	Genoa	20	Vying
26	Digs	22	Dirk

Solutions 53–54

53

Across:

1 Want
4 Dons
8 Hoop (Won ton soup)
9 Status quo
11 Gravid
13 Almanac
15 Lesser
16 Thirst
18 Turnip
20 Breeze
22 Armadas
23 Relate
25 Effective
26 Orgy
27 Brag
28 Yard

Down:

2 Ante
3 Totals
4 Disbar
5 Nougat
6 Converses
7 Spud
10 Orchard
12 Slot
13 Astrology
14 Mediate
17 Tier
19 Prefer
20 Bad egg
21 Earthy
23 Room
24 Aver

54

Across:

1 Car
3 Mum
5 Bare (Camembert)
7 Piles
8 Reside
10 Team
11 Virtuous
13 Lotion
14 Deduce
17 Together
19 Bias
21 Famine
22 Whole
23 Once
24 Toy
25 Mat

Down:

1 Capitulate
2 Reliant
3 Mesh
4 Morbid
5 Besotted
6 Radio
9 Assessment
12 Contrite
15 Uniform
16 Defect
18 Grain
20 Sway

Solutions 55–56

55

Across:

1 Filler
4 Steins (Philistines)
9 Might
10 Swollen
11 Eat
12 Utter
13 Angrier
15 Circulation
19 Regions
20 Sharp
21 Ham
22 Imagine
24 Olive
25 Garage
26 Reined

Down:

1 Famous
2 Lightning
3 Enter
5 Thought
6 Ill
7 Sentry
8 Established
14 Isolation
16 Closing
17 Trying
18 Spread
20 Smoke
23 Air

56

Across:

1 Sir
3 Pry
5 Sing (Surprising)
7 Inner
8 Liquid
10 Brat
11 Coherent
13 Likely
14 Eczema
17 Taciturn
19 Yuri
21 Belief
22 Nudes
23 Jeer
24 Box
25 Ray

Down:

1 Shibboleth
2 Ransack
3 Pure
4 Yellow
5 Sequence
6 Naive
9 Stravinsky
12 Clothier
15 Ecuador
16 Prefab
18 Crete
20 Onyx

Solutions 57–58

57

Across:

1 Hew
3 Mainly (Humanely)
7 Novices
8 Proof
10 Minx
11 Jubilant
13 Leader
15 Poodle
17 Youthful
18 Idol
21 Drier
22 Horizon
23 Ogress
24 Bin

Down:

1 Haven
2 Wick
3 Mosque
4 Imprison
5 Leopard
6 Unemployed
9 Fatherland
12 Sea horse
14 Amusing
16 Bushes
19 Dozen
20 Grub

58

Across:

1 Hal
3 Loose
6 Sin
8 Asian (Hallucination)
9 Cash cow
10 Imbecility
12 Zap
15 Tact
17 Keep
18 Kit
22 Profitable
25 Arsenic
26 Plaid
27 Toy
28 Hit on
29 Dud

Down:

1 Hyacinth
2 Laid-back
3 Lunacy
4 Occult
5 Ersatz
6 Sock
7 Newt
11 Yak
13 Pegboard
14 Splendid
16 Tip
19 Trench
20 Offcut
21 Stop in
23 Vast
24 Espy

Solutions 59–60

59

Across:
1 Cheque
4 Curd
9 Korea (Chequered career)
10 Replica
11 Salient
12 Extol
13 Pigsty
15 Sniper
18 Cobra
20 Mafioso
23 Leaflet
24 Leech
25 Lurk
26 Bootee

Down:
1 Cakes
2 Earplug
3 Ukase
5 Umpteen
6 Drift
7 Wrath
8 Tailor
13 Pickle
14 Trawler
16 Project
17 Emote
19 Brawl
21 Folio
22 Ochre

60

Across:
1 Pane
3 Stake
7 King (Painstaking)
8 Decree nisi
9 Noel
12 Shoestrings
13 Route
15 Agony
19 Encouraging
21 Nero
23 Transplant
24 Disc
25 Hiker
26 Skis

Down:
1 Pedestrian
2 Earnest
3 Siesta
4 Acidic
5 Eking
6 Once
10 Oslo
11 Laryngitis
14 User
16 Goggles
17 Mohawk
18 Eraser
20 Notch
22 Exit

Solutions 61–62

61

Across:		Down:	
1	Caught	1	Careless
7	Marshal (Court martial)	2	Ultimate
8	Retorted	3	Heron
9	Lucky	4	Dad
10	Lemon	5	Assume
11	Adam	6	Walker
12	Zebra	7	Melancholic
15	Decay	9	Lazy
16	Siege	13	Bachelor
19	Echo	14	Anecdote
20	Ethic	15	Deck
21	Stink	17	Intent
22	Vindaloo	18	Gender
23	Endemic	20	Endow
24	Swerve	22	Via

62

Across:		Down:	
1	Quay	1	Quail
3	Wheeze (Kiwis)	2	Artless
9	Attempt	4	Humanitarian
10	Maize	5	Exist
11	Lie	6	Eternal
12	Orpington	7	Impoverished
13	Jester	8	Stop
14	Stroll	13	Jukebox
16	Kissinger	15	Offhand
19	Fig	17	Stern
21	Beech	18	Glut
22	Unaware	20	Great
23	Xanadu		
24	Edit		

Solutions 63–64

63

Across:

1	Turner
5	Weigh (Turn away)
9	Tolerance
10	Pal
11	Nut
12	Abandoned
14	Gap
16	Award
18	Ely
19	Acrobatic
21	Spa
22	Hog
23	Advantage
25	Range
26	Mayhem

Down:

2	Unlit
3	Nirvana
4	Run
5	Wield
6	Impinge
7	Holidaymaker
8	Stenographer
13	Adapt
15	Paragon
17	Decency
20	Brace
21	Stale
24	Vim

64

Across:

1	Sigh
4	Defects (Side effects)
8	Remember
9	Ail
11	Talent
13	Casino
14	Grill
15	Earn
17	Type
18	Dingy
20	Widget
21	Secret
24	Roc
25	Preamble
26	Diluted
27	Nose

Down:

2	Ideal
3	Hoeing
4	Dabs
5	Formal
6	Charity
7	Silhouette
10	Otherworld
12	Trait
13	Clogs
16	Radical
18	Despot
19	Yeoman
22	Riles
23	Feud

Solutions 65–66

65

Across:
1 Sun
3 Tall
5 Buns (St Albans)
8 Announce
10 Deep
11 Gas
13 Tidal
14 Parchment
16 Ale
17 Nan
19 Onslaught
21 Plain
22 Tar
24 Pain
25 Homicide
26 Sent
27 Cede
28 Try

Down:
1 Stag
2 Nuns
3 Truncheons
4 Locate
6 Unending
7 Supplant
9 Natal
12 Attractive
14 Pan-pipes
15 Relation
18 Ahead
20 Strode
22 Tilt
23 Rely

66

Across:
1 Neigh
4 Kid
6 Aye (Naked eye)
8 Callisthenics
9 Totem
11 Rice
13 Eaten
14 Pager
15 Horde
16 Edge
18 Roses
21 Corpus Christi
23 Pal
24 Bap
25 Maybe

Down:
1 Nectar
2 Idle
3 Hoist
4 Kit
5 Dreamer
6 Agitated
7 Ensign
10 Togas
12 Corporal
14 Perturb
15 Hiccup
17 Excise
19 Serum
20 Espy
22 Cop

Solutions 67–68

67

Across:

1	Pry
3	Fit
5	High (Private Eye)
7	Drank
8	Random
10	Sane
11	Pitiless
13	Riddle
14	Baffle
17	Abnormal
19	Loss
21	Ardour
22	Agile
23	Mess
24	Cut
25	Hot

Down:

1	Pedestrian
2	Yearned
3	Fake
4	Torrid
5	Handicap
6	Globe
9	Assessment
12	Glorious
15	Foolish
16	Fabric
18	Nerve
20	Rant

68

Across:

7	Polled
8	Answer (Pole dancer)
10	Camelot
11	Dozen
12	Roux
13	Scene
17	Fight
18	Wish
22	Homer
23	Lacquer
24	Legato
25	Greece

Down:

1	Spectre
2	Glamour
3	Jelly
4	Anodyne
5	Swizz
6	Trunk
9	Stockholm
14	Vibrate
15	Bitumen
16	Charmer
19	Whale
20	Image
21	Score

Solutions 69–70

69

Across:
1 Fie
3 Fun
5 Dread (Five hundred)
8 Novel
9 Memoirs
10 Yale
11 Quencher
13 Rupert
14 Injury
17 Uxorious
19 Piaf
22 Ammeter
23 Wrong
24 Barmy
25 Zen
26 Nun

Down:
1 Fancy
2 Envelop
3 Folk
4 Nimbus
5 Dominant
6 Edith
7 Destroy
12 Artistry
13 Rhubarb
15 Unicorn
16 Quartz
18 Ormer
20 Fagin
21 Swan

70

Across:
1 Autumn
5 Attic (Automatic)
9 Rhapsodic
10 Pie
11 Sue
12 Albatross
14 Alb
16 Taboo
18 Amp
19 Chauffeur
21 Fir
22 Eat
23 Catamaran
25 Rebus
26 Panama

Down:
2 Usage
3 Upstart
4 Nod
5 Ascot
6 Tapioca
7 Cheeseparing
8 Crystal clear
13 Bible
15 Bran tub
17 Oarsman
20 Focus
21 Forum
24 Tip

Solutions 71–72

71

Across:

1 Judge
4 Meant
8 Awl (Judgmental)
9 Prehistoric
10 Nuptial
12 Deign
13 Effigy
14 Assize
17 Frail
19 Eternal
21 Disbeliever
23 Cue
24 Rhyme
25 Fetch

Down:

1 Japan
2 Doe
3 Exiting
4 Mettle
5 Acrid
6 Tactician
7 Al dente
11 Puff adder
13 Enforce
15 Sheriff
16 Recede
18 Lusty
20 Larch
22 Vat

72

Across:

1 Reign
4 Cheque (Rain check)
9 Flummox
10 Miami
11 Leek
12 Central
13 Jut
14 Gala
16 Talk
18 Pry
20 Macabre
21 Idea
24 Swear
25 Content
26 Dither
27 Polly

Down:

1 Raffle
2 Inure
3 Name
5 Humanity
6 Quarrel
7 Edible
8 Exact
13 Jamboree
15 Ancient
17 Amused
18 Peace
19 Pantry
22 Dwell
23 Snap

Solutions 73–74

73

Across:
1 Throne
4 Over
9 Bored (Thrown overboard)
10 Apricot
11 Ambient
12 Idyll
13 Astute
15 Cousin
18 Lucid
20 Larceny
23 Zealous
24 Dodge
25 Step
26 Horrid

Down:
1 Tibia
2 Rarebit
3 Nudge
5 Vertigo
6 Rocky
7 Party
8 Stolen
13 Ablaze
14 Tadpole
16 Slender
17 Close
19 Chaos
21 Radio
22 Yield

74

Across:
1 Knee
5 Pall (Nepal)
7 Praline
8 Thickset
10 Iffy
12 Agog
14 Run short
16 Canister
17 Reap
18 Chin
19 Quayside
22 Swindle
23 Mess
24 Deft

Down:
1 Kant
2 Epic
3 Sanskrit
4 Diet
5 Perisher
6 Lily
9 Hogwash
11 Forward
13 Grimness
15 Normandy
18 Calm
19 Quip
20 Shed
21 Exit

Solutions 75–76

75

Across:

1 Waste
3 Banned (Waistband)
7 Vandalism
9 Feel
10 Term
11 Apron
13 Extort
14 Windy
15 Gloom
17 Soccer
20 Wagon
21 Veto
23 Snub
24 Enjoyment
25 Tucson
26 Speed

Down:

1 Waffle
2 Teal
3 Billow
4 Nest
5 Drama
6 Adapt
7 Ventilate
8 Mendicant
11 Arrow
12 Nixon
16 Maroon
17 Somme
18 Ribald
19 Evert
22 Onus
23 Snip

76

Across:

1 Seize
4 Hide (Seaside)
7 Grip
8 Ordinary
9 Energetic
10 Bet
12 Feeler
14 Entire
16 Ace
18 Sacrilege
21 Plethora
22 Iris
23 Loom
24 Hence

Down:

1 Strange
2 Imperils
3 Erode
4 Hunt
5 Dirge
6 Advise
11 Stallion
13 Reason
15 Ragtime
17 Cello
19 Reach
20 Atom

Solutions 77–78

77

Across:

1 Shawl
5 Heave (Shore leave)
8 Adore
9 Often
10 Gold plate
11 Too
12 Ready-to-wear
15 Temperament
19 Hut
20 Replenish
22 Exile
23 Salsa
24 Satay
25 Dress

Down:

1 Short cut
2 Author
3 Language
4 Motley
5 Heap
6 Arcade
7 Edge
13 Overhead
14 Restless
16 Moppet
17 Avidly
18 Thrice
20 Ruts
21 Easy

78

Across:

1 Key
3 Sent
5 Hell (Kiss and tell)
8 Stricken
10 Mean
11 Sun
13 Realm
14 Commander
16 Era
17 Can
19 Intellect
21 Sheen
22 Lid
24 Rank
25 Escapade
26 Dull
27 Fret
28 Rot

Down:

1 Kiss
2 Yarn
3 Saccharine
4 Needed
6 Elegance
7 Liniment
9 Tutor
12 Irrelevant
14 Censored
15 Maternal
18 Acrid
20 Teaser
22 Lair
23 Debt

Solutions 79–80

79

Across:

1 Lower
4 Slain (Lois Lane)
8 Use
9 Nationalist
10 Habitat
12 Seize
13 Desire
14 Adhere
17 Giant
19 Stretch
21 Duplicitous
23 Due
24 Recce
25 Gaffe

Down:

1 Lynch
2 Wet
3 Rooster
4 Scanty
5 Alias
6 Nutriment
7 Relieve
11 Bystander
13 Degrade
15 Darling
16 Aspire
18 Topic
20 Haste
22 Off

80

Across:

1 Knock
4 Terns (Nocturnes)
8 Ado
9 Full-blooded
10 Adjourn
12 Eclat
13 Piazza
14 Sombre
17 Roost
19 Engaged
21 Aeolian harp
23 Err
24 Credo
25 Comet

Down:

1 Kafka
2 Owl
3 Kibbutz
4 Thorny
5 Ridge
6 Saddlebag
7 Mountie
11 Joan of Arc
13 Parquet
15 Organic
16 Mexico
18 Trove
20 Depot
22 Arm

Solutions 81–82

81

Across:

1 Sicker
4 Fancy (Sycophancy)
8 Blaze
9 Proffer
10 Lighter
11 Typo
12 Kew
14 Ergo
15 Rope
18 Nip
21 Luck
23 Luggage
25 Quavers
26 Leapt
27 Empty
28 Writer

Down:

1 Subtle
2 Charger
3 Exertion
4 Food
5 Nifty
6 Yarrow
7 Spark
13 Wriggler
16 Peasant
17 Clique
19 Plush
20 Jester
22 Cramp
24 Levy

82

Across:

1 Yew
3 Knee
5 Klee (Uniquely)
8 Rheostat
10 Scot
11 Eek
13 Lance
14 Needfully
16 Inn
17 Ego
19 Itchy feet
21 Grief
22 Ask
24 Idea
25 Kedgeree
26 Gore
27 Meet
28 Den

Down:

1 Yore
2 Week
3 Kiss of life
4 Enamel
6 Licensee
7 Entrepot
9 Helen
12 Fly-by-night
14 Niggling
15 Engineer
18 Geese
20 Cheese
22 Arid
23 Keen

Solutions 83–84

83

Across:

1 Caper
4 Ceilidh (Capercaillie)
8 Hay
9 Toddy
10 Gremlin
11 Cinderella
14 Morass
16 Tycoon
18 Maraschino
22 Amazing
23 Dozen
24 Lee
25 Lineage
26 Tarka

Down:

1 Catacomb
2 Pedantry
3 Rhyme
4 Cygnet
5 Ideally
6 Idle
7 Hank
12 Howitzer
13 Insomnia
15 Stamina
17 Wangle
19 Cadet
20 Mail
21 Lawn

84

Across:

4 Feller
5 Part (Fell apart)
7 Cowered
10 Eager
11 Reliant
12 Tenor
14 Stature
15 Khaki
16 Illness
20 Title
21 Titania
22 Ewer
23 Velvet

Down:

1 Alter
2 Jewel
3 Manatee
4 Flog
6 Tremor
8 Reptile
9 Distant
10 Entrust
13 Choice
14 Skilled
17 Eider
18 Salvo
19 List

Solutions 85–86

85

Across:
1 Penny
4 Tense (Penitence)
10 Natural
11 Siren
12 Cargo
13 Samovar
15 Used
17 Lasso
19 Early
22 Find
25 Almanac
27 Macaw
29 Court
30 Narrate
31 Cycle
32 Sloth

Down:
2 Enter
3 Nervous
5 Epsom
6 Shrivel
7 Snack
8 Close
9 Angry
14 Aden
16 Sofa
18 Armoury
20 Admiral
21 Match
23 Icing
24 Owner
26 Natal
28 Chart

86

Across:
1 Whine
4 Wrack (Wine rack)
8 Sweeper
9 Ridge
10 Entertainment
11 Entire
12 Grumpy
15 Sit on the fence
18 Geese
19 Risotto
20 Theme
21 Dirty

Down:
1 Waste
2 Identity theft
3 Emperor
4 Warsaw
5 Apron
6 Kidderminster
7 Sentry
11 Ensign
13 Refused
14 Charge
16 Niece
17 Ebony

Solutions 87–88

87

Across:

1 Fizzy
4 Cysts (Physicists)
8 Utrillo
9 Moose
10 Praying mantis
11 On high
12 Modern
15 Edgar Allan Poe
18 Steam
19 Maitre d
20 Kitty
21 Nadir

Down:

1 Frump
2 Zorba the Greek
3 Yelling
4 Chough
5 Samba
6 Short-tempered
7 Reason
11 Or else
13 Ovation
14 Clumsy
16 Remit
17 Eider

88

Across:

1 Salver
4 Door
9 Dally (Salvador Dali)
10 Get lost
11 Epistle
12 Crypt
13 Gaggle
15 Blasts
18 Realm
20 Innards
23 Episode
24 Ruler
25 Gong
26 Reason

Down:

1 Sidle
2 Lulling
3 Egypt
5 Optical
6 Roomy
7 Agree
8 Status
13 Garret
14 Lampoon
16 Surplus
17 Cited
19 Aping
21 Nurse
22 Siren

Solutions 89–90

89

Across:		Down:	
1	Pass	1	Practising
3	Chair	2	Synapse
7	Eyes (Pasteurise)	3	Choirs
8	Abandoning	4	Aviary
9	Apes	5	Regal
12	Temporarily	6	Cede
13	Sired	10	Pyre
15	Crepe	11	Speechless
19	Standoffish	14	Rosy
21	Goya	16	Reforms
23	Plagiarise	17	Unfair
24	Ease	18	Copies
25	Sorts	20	Tapes
26	Sins	22	Oral

90

Across:		Down:	
1	Toe	1	Tomahawk
3	Stand	2	Edgewise
6	Mar	3	Sitcom
8	Might (Toast and Marmite)	4	Ask for
9	Kick-off	5	Decade
10	How do you do	6	Mood
12	Eft	7	Rift
15	Wisp	11	Off
17	Frog	13	Traverse
18	Elk	14	Agrarian
22	Yugoslavia	16	Ply
25	Gas main	19	Kuwait
26	Corgi	20	Horned
27	Err	21	Plucky
28	Toddy	23	Ogre
29	Eon	24	Tsar

Solutions 91–92

91

Across:
1 Arc
3 Can
5 Sore (Arkansas)
7 Amaze
8 Clique
10 Gust
11 Katmandu
13 Muster
14 Astute
17 The Birds
19 Zeus
21 Scarce
22 Omega
23 Klee
24 Gut
25 Sad

Down:
1 Amalgamate
2 Chassis
3 Chef
4 Nectar
5 Skirmish
6 Rouen
9 Queensland
12 Pedigree
15 Useless
16 Edberg
18 Excel
20 Jolt

92

Across:
1 Vigil
4 Aunties (Vigilantes)
8 Rum
9 Lot
10 Bambi
11 Extra
12 Sweetie
15 Byte
17 Red-eye
19 Earner
22 Take
24 Cowslip
26 Rajah
28 Squad
30 Gas
31 Flu
32 Sincere
33 Lease

Down:
1 Vermeer
2 Gamut
3 Lullaby
4 Attest
5 Noble
6 Ism
7 Seize
13 Week
14 Ton
16 Yeti
18 Dew
20 Aerosol
21 Rehouse
23 Apogee
24 Casks
25 Ledge
27 Jaffa
29 Urn

Solutions 93–94

93

Across:
1 Suck
4 Session (Succession)
8 Chambray
9 Cow
11 Marina
13 Shrine
14 Ozone
15 Roux
17 Heal
18 Arrow
20 Danube
21 Pigeon
24 Nor
25 Ukuleles
26 Everest
27 Yeti

Down:
2 Usher
3 Kimono
4 Surf
5 Scythe
6 Incline
7 New Zealand
10 Imprudence
12 Azure
13 Snoop
16 Unnerve
18 Abjure
19 Winery
22 Elect
23 Quit

94

Across:
1 Gnasher
5 Null
7 Truss (National Trust)
8 Imbibe
10 Sofa
11 Reveller
13 Mortar
14 Sarong
17 Nicotine
19 Judo
21 Garnet
22 Weepy
23 Whet
24 Pipette

Down:
1 Gethsemane
2 Aquifer
3 Host
4 Ruined
5 Nobleman
6 Label
9 Troglodyte
12 Martinet
15 Opulent
16 Instep
18 Clash
20 Swap

Solutions 95–96

95

Across:

1 Spa
3 King
5 Plug (Sparking plug)
8 Great War
10 Onus
11 Hod
13 Umbra
14 Himalayas
16 One
17 Ale
19 Inflicted
21 Incan
22 Eva
24 Zeal
25 Queasier
26 Rota
27 Byre
28 Gay

Down:

1 Sigh
2 Axed
3 Kite-flying
4 Nearly
6 Longboat
7 Gestated
9 Rodin
12 Just in case
14 Howitzer
15 Merchant
18 Leave
20 Floury
22 Eigg
23 Army

96

Across:

1 Carp
4 Entry (Carpentry)
8 Retrieve
9 Each
10 Crow
11 Estimate
12 Strict
14 Ensure
16 Abundant
19 Duty
20 Tour
21 Ignominy
22 Dodge
23 Tiny

Down:

2 Arrow
3 Present
4 Erect
5 Thermos
6 Yacht
7 Ferret
13 Ignored
14 Extinct
15 Rotund
17 Broad
18 Agile
19 Demon

Solutions 97–98

97

Across:
1 High
4 Pot
6 Inn
9 Use (Hypotenuse)
10 Amaze
11 About
12 Abandoned
15 Inexperienced
19 Operative
21 Brief
22 Usual
24 Ass
25 Ewe
26 Eon
27 Shed

Down:
2 Iterate
3 Hoard
4 Pea
5 Treadle
6 Igloo
7 Neat
8 Lunatic
13 Nurse
14 Adverse
16 Profuse
17 Climate
18 Aisle
20 Atlas
21 Base
23 Urn

98

Across:
1 Par
3 Kiss
5 Tarn (Pakistan)
8 Estonian
10 Snub
11 Ape
13 Enrol
14 Swaziland
16 End
17 Act
19 Hopefully
21 Olive
22 Ant
24 Iris
25 Sinister
26 Anna
27 Thus
28 Pop

Down:
1 Plea
2 Rate
3 Kingfisher
4 Sparta
6 Abnormal
7 Nobility
9 Spawn
12 Bed of nails
14 Semolina
15 Addition
18 Clone
20 Pariah
22 Atop
23 Trip

Solutions 99–100

99

Across:

1 Four
3 Tess
9 Queue (Fortescue)
10 Impromptu
11 Enter
12 Periscope
15 Nausea
17 Secure
19 Playhouse
21 Rifle
23 Reputable
24 Cargo
25 Rare
26 Arid

Down:

1 Flippant
2 Uppercut
4 Employ
5 Squeeze
6 Left
7 Dear
8 Toss
13 Cucumber
14 Reverend
16 Emperor
18 Pamper
20 Hate
21 Rich
22 Fury

100

Across:

1 Aunt
3 Surf
6 Own (Answerphone)
9 Tongue-twister
10 Outsmart
12 Note
13 Nag
15 Impend
18 Rudely
19 Tot
21 Aged
22 Subsonic
25 Incommunicado
26 End
27 Nets
28 Dhal

Down:

1 Authoritative
2 Nonet
4 Upturn
5 Fail
6 Outcome
7 Nursery school
8 Augment
11 Tar
14 Gunship
16 Pierced
17 Dos
20 Tumult
23 Neath
24 Omen

Solutions 101–102

101

Across:

1 Asti
3 Kiwi
6 Kit (A sticky wicket)
9 Curtain raiser
10 Insulate
12 Brio
13 Egg
15 Esteem
18 Oodles
19 Dam
21 Trap
22 Padlocks
25 Reprehensible
26 Lie
27 Kept
28 Real

Down:

1 Architectural
2 Terms
4 Ignite
5 Imam
6 Kestrel
7 Tortoiseshell
8 Vaulted
11 Ego
14 Godless
16 Trample
17 Map
20 Made up
23 Cable
24 Seek

102

Across:

1 Yearn
4 Gut
6 Art (Young at heart)
8 Procrastinate
9 Evens
11 Duct
13 Tooth
14 Ditty
15 Since
16 Grip
18 Sharp
21 Instantaneous
23 End
24 Rug
25 Abode

Down:

1 Yapped
2 Avow
3 Nerve
4 Gas
5 Thirsty
6 Abattoir
7 Trench
10 Extra
12 Confused
14 Despair
15 Scribe
17 Pursue
19 Panda
20 Solo
22 Tag

Solutions 103–104

103

Across:

1	Pier
3	Steers (Pierced ears)
8	Strange
9	Gauge
10	Abhor
11	Terrify
12	Elated
14	Recess
18	Inexact
20	Pupil
22	Loath
23	Purloin
24	Ceased
25	Edge

Down:

1	Passage
2	Earth
3	Sleuth
4	Eager
5	Routine
6	Untrue
7	Very
13	Average
15	Expire
16	Silence
17	Stupid
18	Idle
19	Ashes
21	Proud

104

Across:

1	Hurley
4	Burred (Early bird)
7	Kampuchea
9	Vend
10	Flop
11	Cedes
13	Dawdle
14	Reject
15	Satrap
17	Quince
19	Revue
20	Lilt
22	Atom
23	Lassitude
24	Resign
25	Dreamy

Down:

1	Halved
2	Lead
3	Yippee
4	Bicker
5	Reef
6	Despot
7	Know-it-all
8	Alternate
11	Clear
12	Segue
15	Silver
16	Person
17	Quoted
18	Enmity
21	Taxi
22	Adze

Solutions 105–106

105

Across:

1 Reign
4 Cheque (Rain check)
9 Rustler
10 Skimp
11 Tank
12 Freezer
13 Jot
14 Peru
16 Rude
18 Dry
20 Robbery
21 Shah
24 Corgi
25 Anagram
26 Yeomen
27 Dress

Down:

1 Rarity
2 Ibsen
3 Nile
5 Hostelry
6 Quizzed
7 Expert
8 Graft
13 Juvenile
15 Embargo
17 Tricky
18 Dylan
19 Thomas
22 Horde
23 Ward

106

Across:

1 Mars
4 Cap
6 Pony
8 Cheese (Mascarpone cheese)
9 Minute
10 Knothole
11 Curd
12 Guided missile
17 Scar
19 Colonist
22 Butter
23 Within
24 Whey
25 Mud
26 Milk

Down:

2 Ashen
3 Scented
4 Credo
5 Pompeii
6 Panic
7 Natural
10 Keg
13 Uncouth
14 Decorum
15 Sanctum
16 Eat
18 Ratty
20 Lowed
21 Swirl

Solutions 107–108

107

Across:

1 Thyme
4 Lourdes (Time Lords)
8 Erg
9 Cur
10 Cameo
11 McCoy
12 Circlet
15 Peso
17 Siesta
19 Tenant
22 Sham
24 Pertwee
26 Baker
28 Trout
30 Ton
31 Ali
32 Rancher
33 Smith

Down:

1 Thermos
2 Yogic
3 Encrypt
4 Lyrics
5 Ulcer
6 Dim
7 Scout
13 Iota
14 Lea
16 Ease
18 Ear
20 Embanks
21 Tarnish
23 Hector
24 Peter
25 Witch
27 Khaki
29 Own

108

Across:

1 Buy
3 Awl
5 Means (By all means)
8 Opera
9 Sincere
10 Hide
11 Merchant
13 Abduct
14 Recede
17 Acquired
19 Used
22 Amateur
23 Theme
24 Theft
25 Yaw
26 Nil

Down:

1 Booth
2 Yielded
3 Alas
4 Lessen
5 Manacles
6 Arena
7 Spectre
12 Accident
13 Adamant
15 Eastern
16 Betray
18 Quake
20 Dwell
21 Stow

Solutions 109–110

109

Across:

1 Cart
3 Blanch (Carte blanche)
9 Sapient
10 Grill
11 Emu
12 Reputedly
13 Clergy
14 Amazon
16 Important
19 Axe
21 About
22 Callous
23 Effort
24 I spy

Down:

1 Caste
2 Rapture
4 Legitimately
5 Naiad
6 Halcyon
7 Refrigerator
8 Step
13 Climate
15 Zealous
17 Proof
18 Arch
20 Essay

110

Across:

1 Queue
4 Doss (Kudos)
8 Act
9 Impulsive
10 Trap
11 Frontier
12 Pot
13 Meagre
14 Finger
16 Bid
17 Transfer
18 Snag
20 Razorbill
21 Owl
22 Mend
23 Miser

Down:

1 Quantum
2 Extravaganza
3 Exit
4 Depart
5 Splendid
6 Disingenuous
7 Dear
11 Foe
12 Preserve
14 Fir
15 Regular
16 Behind
17 Term
19 Glum

Solutions 111–112

111

Across:
1 Moll
4 Dover (Moldova)
8 Old fogey
9 Gull
10 Tsar
11 Penzance
12 Darwin
14 Jotter
16 Question
19 Buck
20 Thor
21 Futility
22 Ruler
23 Reek

Down:
2 Offer
3 Leg spin
4 Doyen
5 Vagrant
6 Relic
7 Plasma
13 Wastrel
14 Janitor
15 Excite
17 Usher
18 Infer
19 Bulge

112

Across:
1 Oak
3 Ache
5 Oral (OK Corral)
8 Provence
10 Flag
11 Sit
13 Avail
14 Dishonest
16 Ode
17 Lot
19 Artillery
21 Exalt
22 Beg
24 Toil
25 Baseball
26 Chew
27 Cost
28 End

Down:
1 Oops
2 Knot
3 Ameliorate
4 Heckle
6 Reliable
7 Legality
9 Rigid
12 Battlement
14 Domestic
15 Sedative
18 Oriel
20 Tomato
22 Base
23 Glad

Solutions 113–114

113

Across:

1 Quito
4 Thud
8 Awe (Key to the door)
9 Affiliate
10 Ripe
11 Feckless
12 Pie
13 Lariat
14 Sluice
16 Fly
17 Over play
18 Ague
20 Kickbacks
21 Ova
22 Zest
23 Yield

Down:

1 Quarrel
2 Inexperience
3 Oral
4 Toffee
5 Unlikely
6 Watering hole
7 Jets
11 Fit
12 Palpable
14 Sly
15 Emerald
16 Faucet
17 Oiks
19 Espy

114

Across:

7 Sack
8 Ray
9 Blur (Sacré bleu!)
10 Pompom
11 Try-out
12 Ill
13 Ankles
14 Esteem
16 Cactus
19 Astute
21 Wad
22 Muesli
24 Devoid
25 Memo
26 Ewe
27 Tyke

Down:

1 Lagoon
2 Sky pilot
3 Aramis
4 Myrtle
5 Obey
6 Suture
15 Titivate
17 Amulet
18 Swivel
19 Addled
20 Tricky
23 Soot

Solutions 115–116

115

Across:
1 Know
4 Hulk
8 Hard (Noël Coward)
9 Loathsome
11 Blonde
13 Severed
15 Astral
16 Reason
18 Sortie
20 Fleece
22 Annoyed
23 Silent
25 Transient
26 Rant
27 Opus
28 Rash

Down:
2 Noon
3 Wither
4 Hostel
5 Limber
6 Garnished
7 Edge
10 Elderly
12 Lass
13 Startling
14 Valiant
17 Need
19 Entrap
20 Founds
21 Eerier
23 Sore
24 Ants

116

Across:
1 Queue
4 Ritz (Curates)
8 Offbeat
9 Odour
10 Egret
11 Yoghurt
13 Amends
15 Driver
17 Excerpt
20 Lover
22 Sonny
23 Planned
24 Keep
25 Tripe

Down:
1 Quote
2 Effervescent
3 Ejected
4 Ratty
5 Thong
6 Modus vivendi
7 Writer
12 Odd
13 Ageism
14 Sop
16 Reliant
18 Rhyme
19 Top-up
21 Ridge

Solutions 117–118

117

Across:
1 Moaner
4 Leaser (Mona Lisa)
7 Querulous
9 Onus
10 Move
11 Alter
13 Artery
14 Sachet
15 Bottom
17 Forced
19 Wigan
20 Roof
22 Sect
23 Nightcaps
24 Snazzy
25 Annexe

Down:
1 Mimosa
2 Nous
3 Rarely
4 Lilies
5 Alum
6 Reject
7 Quotation
8 Sophocles
11 Arrow
12 Rayon
15 Burkas
16 Mighty
17 Fascia
18 Dotage
21 Fizz
22 Spin

118

Across:
1 Reign
5 Beaux (Rainbow)
8 Osier
9 Tudor
10 Telegrams
11 Egg
12 Overturning
15 Human dynamo
19 Red
20 Beer belly
22 Inner
23 Scorn
24 Evict
25 Green

Down:
1 Retrench
2 Indigo
3 Northern
4 Violet
5 Brag
6 Alkali
7 Xmas
13 Readying
14 Gridiron
16 Muesli
17 Yellow
18 Orange
20 Blue
21 Bust

Solutions 119–120

119

Across:		Down:	
1	Camp	1	Cenotaph
3	Anne	2	Mackerel
9	Ology (Campanology)	4	Nantes
10	Nocturnal	5	Eoliths
11	Inner	6	Join
12	Treatment	7	Dyer
15	Preach	8	Bust
17	Astern	13	Recoiled
19	Vexatious	14	Angstrom
21	Quota	16	Cavalry
23	Leg-puller	18	Oxygen
24	Incur	20	Tour
25	Yank	21	Quiz
26	Adam	22	Once

120

Across:		Down:	
1	Pillar	1	Possum
4	Torque (Pillow talk)	2	Loop
7	Conceited	3	Recipe
9	Snap	4	Trivia
10	Leap	5	Reel
11	Optic	6	Elapse
13	Menace	7	Carnivore
14	Allege	8	Dependant
15	Devour	11	Occur
17	Random	12	Clean
19	Raven	15	Dreary
20	Ezra	16	Ratify
22	Snub	17	Relief
23	Efficient	18	Mobile
24	Yearly	21	Afar
25	Figure	22	Snag

Solutions 121–122

121

Across:
1 Fiddle
5 Styx (Fiddlesticks)
8 Less
9 Reindeer
10 Plaice
11 Denude
12 Disappeared
15 Abrupt
17 Depart
19 Accident
20 Ugly
21 Fete
22 Dreary

Down:
2 Ideal
3 Dismiss
4 Eerie
5 Sedan
6 Yielded
7 Riddle
12 Debacle
13 Putter
14 Rapture
16 Unite
17 Dated
18 Ruler

122

Across:
1 Bore
3 Knee
6 Owe (Borneo)
9 Remote control
10 Shoulder
12 Sing
13 Lap
15 Enlist
18 With it
19 Hit
21 Tick
22 Capuchin
25 Objectionable
26 Pew
27 Rife
28 Stet

Down:
1 Bird's-nest soup
2 Romeo
4 Nickel
5 Erne
6 Ogreish
7 Enlightenment
8 Stylish
11 Raw
14 Piquant
16 Lockjaw
17 Tic
20 Tariff
23 Habit
24 Scar

Solutions 123–124

123

Across:
1 Hoarse
5 Meet (Horsemeat)
8 Stop
9 Infernal
10 Indict
11 Ritual
12 Flamboyance
15 Trader
17 Superb
19 Minister
20 Utah
21 Feel
22 Dreamy

Down:
2 Often
3 Replica
4 Exist
5 Merit
6 Emanate
7 Affray
12 Fertile
13 Berate
14 Neptune
16 Drill
17 Shred
18 Realm

124

Across:
1 Moats
5 Heart (Mozart)
8 Adieu
9 Abbot
10 Unwitting
11 Ups
12 Heavyweight
15 Slave-driver
19 Urn
20 Spartacus
22 Audit
23 Prong
24 Boots
25 Earth

Down:
1 Measures
2 Ambush
3 Saturate
4 Airway
5 Hurt
6 Ailing
7 Tang
13 Envisage
14 Top-notch
16 Adagio
17 Reckon
18 Rudder
20 Snub
21 Taps

Solutions 125–126

125

Across:

1 Stark
4 Lustre (Star cluster)
9 Orbit
10 Breadth
11 Detract
12 Swede
14 Ray
15 Lax
16 Dry
18 Arc
21 Buyer
22 Torment
23 Ovation
25 Cater
26 Broker
27 Style

Down:

1 Shoddy
2 Arbitrary
3 Kitbag
5 Uneasy
6 Tad
7 Echoes
8 Obstructing
13 Earnestly
17 Absorb
18 Arrive
19 Traces
20 Starve
24 Ado

126

Across:

1 War
3 Tub
5 Head (Water bed)
7 Timid
8 Resign
10 Dive
11 Comedown
13 Allied
14 Finish
17 Atrocity
19 Apes
21 Differ
22 Aroma
23 Hell
24 Yes
25 Eat

Down:

1 Withdrawal
2 Removal
3 Tidy
4 Borrow
5 Hysteria
6 Aggro
9 Enthusiast
12 Merciful
15 Improve
16 Sturdy
18 Raise
20 Lass

Solutions 127–128

127

Across:
1 Teller
4 Storey (Tell a story)
9 Admit
10 Elastic
11 Rim
12 Essay
13 Predict
15 Countryside
19 Chemist
20 Bacon
21 Use
22 Angrier
24 Attic
25 Sentry
26 Chases

Down:
1 Traced
2 Limestone
3 Entry
5 Traders
6 Rat
7 Yachts
8 Temperature
14 Indicates
16 Noisier
17 Scraps
18 Knocks
20 Beach
23 Gun

128

Across:
1 Made
3 Henley (Maidenly)
9 Unequal
10 Copes
11 End
12 Amsterdam
13 Bandit
14 Hijack
16 Catharsis
19 Pet
21 Miami
22 Execute
23 Saying
24 Feud

Down:
1 Mauve
2 Dresden
4 Ecclesiastes
5 Lipid
6 Yashmak
7 Humanitarian
8 Alas
13 Becomes
15 Ampoule
17 Toady
18 Suez
20 Tweed

Solutions 129–130

129

Across:
1 Wether
4 Fork
9 Astor (Weather forecaster)
10 Wallace
11 Kindred
12 Quell
13 Jackal
15 Meadow
18 Night
20 Laconic
23 Excused
24 Razor
25 Oink
26 Points

Down:
1 Whack
2 Titanic
3 Error
5 Oblique
6 Knave
7 Swede
8 Yellow
13 Junket
14 Artisan
16 Denizen
17 Blade
19 Gecko
21 Cargo
22 Corps

130

Across:
1 Axe
3 Sea
5 Dent (Accident)
7 Tally
8 Reside
10 Rove
11 Bass drum
13 Hungry
14 Serbia
17 Calamity
19 Luck
21 Scanty
22 Lodge
23 Idol
24 Raw
25 Rat

Down:
1 Aftershock
2 Enliven
3 Soya
4 Abroad
5 Disaster
6 Nadir
9 Embankment
12 Criminal
15 Blunder
16 Stayer
18 Laced
20 Blow

Solutions 131–132

131

Across:
1 Cross
4 Whirred
8 Scent
9 Tenniel (Crossword Centennial)
10 Arsenal
11 Binge
12 Dressy
14 Jester
18 Forum
20 Archaic
22 Reverie
23 Blini
24 Evening
25 Legit

Down:
1 Custard
2 Oversee
3 Satin
4 Wattle
5 Ignoble
6 Reign
7 Delve
13 Samurai
15 Trading
16 Receipt
17 Bad egg
18 Forge
19 Revue
21 Cabal

132

Across:
7 Tapped
8 Answer (Tap dancer)
10 Bargain
11 Unrig
13 Even
15 Abyss
17 Decay
19 Talk
23 Zebra
25 Matador
26 Resist
27 Cygnet

Down:
1 Stable
2 Sparse
3 Delay
4 Anguish
5 Ewer
6 Brag
9 Snub
12 Ideal
14 Value
16 Because
18 Acme
20 Ardent
21 Karate
22 Stays
23 Zero
24 Bash

Solutions 133–134

133

Across:
1 Eggs
3 Horse
7 Size (Exorcise)
8 Horrendous
9 Aura
12 Blind alleys
13 Towed
15 Cadge
19 Reservation
21 Node
23 Retirement
24 Sari
25 Empty
26 Told

Down:
1 Exhibition
2 Strange
3 Hangar
4 Rootle
5 Essay
6 Czar
10 Used
11 Alternated
14 Ward
16 Attempt
17 Pent-up
18 Overly
20 Eerie
22 Opal

134

Across:
1 Laud
4 Mare (Lord Mayor)
8 Oboe
9 Derringer
11 Ferret
13 Take out
15 Dormer
16 Likely
18 Effete
20 Author
22 Rubbery
23 Salver
25 Lohengrin
26 Flat
27 Pert
28 Calf

Down:
2 Apex
3 Durham
4 Manger
5 Rueful
6 Abernethy
7 Feat
10 Retinue
12 Idle
13 Trafalgar
14 Kestrel
17 Yard
19 Europe
20 Absent
21 Tragic
23 Soft
24 Mill

Solutions 135–136

135

Across:		Down:	
1	Sent	2	Echo
4	Nick	3	Trifle
8	Alas (Saint Nicholas)	4	Notice
9	Christmas	5	Chaser
11	Strive	6	Sleighing
13	Glacier	7	Isle
15	Phoebe	10	Strange
16	Rather	12	Epic
18	Cupola	13	Godparent
20	Agenda	14	Abolish
22	Iceberg	17	Roam
23	Christ	19	Active
25	Hilarious	20	Aboard
26	Rink	21	Ermine
27	Lead	23	Card
28	Even	24	Yule

136

Across:		Down:	
1	Toupee	1	Towns
4	Once	2	Uniform
9	Weigh (To pay one's way)	3	Ether
10	Compare	5	Nominal
11	Scourge	6	Evade
12	Niece	7	Aches
13	Simper	8	Severe
15	Pledge	13	Sewage
18	Whist	14	Extends
20	Headset	16	Discord
23	Grounds	17	Shush
24	Avoid	19	Irons
25	Sash	21	Aware
26	Gender	22	Tudor

Solutions 137–138

137

Across:

1 Swore
4 Muff
7 Lies (Swarm of flies)
8 Coherent
9 Appalling
10 New
12 Frolic
14 Skinny
16 Old
18 Miniature
21 Paradise
22 Alas
23 Keen
24 Lithe

Down:

1 Skipper
2 Obstacle
3 Excel
4 More
5 Fence
6 Thanks
11 Distract
13 Crisis
15 Narrate
17 Leave
19 Ideal
20 Dawn

138

Across:

1 Sloe
3 Butt
9 Shore (Slow but sure)
10 Urban area
11 Repel
12 Hoi polloi
15 Righto
17 Stride
19 Carbuncle
21 Pilot
23 Insolvent
24 Lyric
25 So-so
26 Mend

Down:

1 Southern
2 Oxbridge
4 Unruly
5 Tsarist
6 Soup
7 Peel
8 Info
13 Discrete
14 Dejected
16 Tactics
18 Crisps
20 Ugly
21 Pelt
22 Lark

Solutions 139–140

139

Across:		Down:	
1	Eighteen	1	Epsom
7	Edger (A teenager)	2	Gentile
8	Sensation	3	Thaw
9	Vex	4	Edison
10	Maim	5	Agave
11	Coyote	6	Brixham
13	Quebec	7	Enjoyed
14	Jetsam	12	Feather
17	Obtain	13	Quickly
18	Dump	15	Squeeze
20	Cob	16	Singer
22	Eagerness	17	Obese
23	Loser	19	Posit
24	Browbeat	21	Grow

140

Across:		Down:	
1	Chimneys	1	Cabal
7	Weeps (Chimney sweeps)	2	Isolate
8	Bookmaker	3	Name
9	Own	4	Yokels
10	Lead	5	Devon
11	Flagon	6	Asinine
13	Prefab	7	Wriggle
14	Plaque	12	Javelin
17	Exeter	13	Pretzel
18	Disc	15	Quinine
20	Tea	16	Heaven
22	Invective	17	Earth
23	Eaten	19	Chest
24	Indecent	21	Acre

Solutions 141–142

141

Across:

1 Leader
4 Hosing (Lederhosen)
7 Molluscs
9 Osborne
12 Ethyl
13 Impel
15 Jabot
16 Ashen
17 Yolky
18 Axiom
19 Kitchen
23 Agnostic
24 Wyvern
25 Atonal

Down:

1 Lumberjack
2 All the best
3 Equality
4 Hiss
5 Sago
6 Neon
8 Compiling
10 Rechristen
11 Economical
14 Layabout
20 Iffy
21 Cope
22 Earn

142

Across:

1 Dank
3 Whale (Dan Quayle)
7 Rick
8 Chancellor
9 Oink
12 Purple Heart
13 Eland
15 Ethos
19 Galley proof
21 Dial
23 Vermicelli
24 Dali
25 Nonet
26 Tome

Down:

1 Deciphered
2 Kingpin
3 Weeded
4 Asleep
5 Error
6 Scan
10 Itch
11 Kiss of life
14 Alga
16 Torrent
17 Florin
18 Typist
20 Alvin
22 Imam

Solutions 143–144

143

Across:
1 Acute
4 Raiment (Accoutrement)
8 Hoisted
9 Trite
10 Erect
11 Earnest
13 Lark
15 Espied
17 Instil
20 Zone
22 Dragged
24 Mason
26 Arena
27 Observe
28 Alumnus
29 Scent

Down:
1 Achieve
2 Unite
3 Entitle
4 Rudder
5 Inter
6 Eminent
7 Theft
12 Akin
14 Adze
16 Plateau
18 Nemesis
19 Lenient
21 Odious
22 Drama
23 Grain
25 Surge

144

Across:
1 Sailor
4 Return (Sale or return)
7 Allocate
9 Adamant
12 Deter
13 Roast
15 Large
16 Hound
17 Ditto
18 Rotor
19 Special
23 Valuable
24 Friend
25 Cheers

Down:
1 Scandalous
2 Illiterate
3 Occurred
4 Rued
5 Trim
6 Rain
8 Tarantula
10 Adjustable
11 Tenderness
14 Thorough
20 Peer
21 Core
22 Avid

Solutions 145–146

145

Across:
4 Wether
5 Vain (Weather vane)
7 Caracas
10 Slope
11 Termite
12 Romeo
14 Hadrian
15 Canon
16 Undergo
20 Horde
21 Roedean
22 Sane
23 Actual

Down:
1 Stoat
2 Lehar
3 Galleon
4 Weak
6 Nephew
8 Cezanne
9 Smarter
10 Strange
13 Famous
14 Houdini
17 Roach
18 Odour
19 Fail

146

Across:
1 Digger
4 Whole (Dig a hole)
8 Swamp
9 Outcome
10 Reminds
11 Brag
12 End
14 Free
15 Iron
18 Dye
21 Luck
23 Glanced
25 Worship
26 React
27 Roost
28 Leader

Down:
1 Desire
2 Grammar
3 Expanded
4 Wits
5 Odour
6 Energy
7 Worse
13 Disagree
16 Orchard
17 Flower
19 Egypt
20 Editor
22 Cargo
24 Chat

Solutions 147–148

147

Across:
- **1** Ghetto
- **4** Ferret (Get over it)
- **7** Exterior
- **9** Genteel
- **12** Drown
- **13** Gleam
- **15** Niece
- **16** Elegy
- **17** Domed
- **19** Icing
- **20** Sustain
- **24** Sentient
- **25** Assets
- **26** Gratis

Down:
- **1** Greediness
- **2** Extroverts
- **3** Thronged
- **4** Fire
- **5** Rapt
- **6** Edge
- **8** Ogre
- **10** Experiment
- **11** Laryngitis
- **14** Mediator
- **18** Mine
- **21** Urns
- **22** Tube
- **23** Isis

148

Across:
- **1** Rumour
- **4** Toyed
- **8** Halve
- **9** Writers (Rheumatoid arthritis)
- **10** Set free
- **11** Odds
- **12** Tap
- **14** Case
- **15** Rare
- **18** Dub
- **21** Each
- **23** Unmoved
- **25** Skylark
- **26** Torso
- **27** Sweet
- **28** Priest

Down:
- **1** Rehash
- **2** Militia
- **3** Unearned
- **4** Twig
- **5** Yield
- **6** Desist
- **7** Owlet
- **13** Promoter
- **16** Reverse
- **17** Census
- **19** Bucks
- **20** Adroit
- **22** Clyde
- **24** Salt

Solutions 149–150

149

Across:
1 True
4 Bad
6 Awe (Troubadour)
8 Disagreement
10 Proper
12 Seldom
13 Level
14 Sash
15 Scut
17 Tunis
19 Opaque
21 Apollo
23 Anna Karenina
24 Ely
25 Yob
26 Yell

Down:
2 Ruinous
3 Enamel
4 Bark
5 Diesel
6 Amend
7 Estimation
9 Episcopate
11 Revue
12 Sepia
16 Colonel
17 Turkey
18 Spinny
20 Annoy
22 Drab

150

Across:
1 Lied
3 Cheers (Light years)
8 Airless
9 Truce
10 Style
11 Avarice
12 Nimble
14 Assets
18 Fantasy
20 Ruler
22 Vicar
23 Average
24 Delete
25 Shot

Down:
1 Liaison
2 Early
3 Casual
4 Extra
5 Routine
6 Reveal
7 Here
13 Manacle
15 Shriek
16 Surfeit
17 Gyrate
18 Five
19 Agree
21 Loath

Solutions 151–152

151

Across:
1 Drive-in
5 Reign (Driving rain)
8 Bodge
9 Taffeta
10 Tally-ho
11 Aztec
12 Quebec
14 On hold
17 Imply
19 Awesome
22 Knavish
23 Joins
24 Nahum
25 Mayenne

Down:
1 Debut
2 Indulge
3 Enemy
4 Notion
5 Refrain
6 Inept
7 Nuanced
12 Quicken
13 Elysium
15 Oxonian
16 Fathom
18 Peach
20 Enjoy
21 Ensue

152

Across:
1 Plague
4 Round (Playground)
8 Alibi
9 Account
10 Croquet
11 Fair
12 Zen
14 Halt
15 Alms
18 Yet
21 Rash
23 Abraham
25 Earmark
26 Trove
27 Latex
28 Brogue

Down:
1 Plaice
2 Arizona
3 Ubiquity
4 Rich
5 Uvula
6 Dotard
7 Waltz
13 Narrator
16 Mah-jong
17 Ordeal
19 Tacky
20 Impede
22 Strut
24 Marx

Solutions 153–154

153

Across:
1 Spied
4 Amman (Spider-Man)
8 Oar
9 Superheroes
10 Yawning
12 Swarm
13 Mallet
14 Dragon
17 Greek
19 Avocado
21 Indomitable
23 Tin
24 Essen
25 Robin

Down:
1 Sissy
2 Imp
3 Dormice
4 Avenge
5 Moons
6 Nostalgia
7 Iron man
11 Wolverine
13 Magneto
15 Rooster
16 Batman
18 Kudos
20 Ocean
22 Bob

154

Across:
1 High
4 Dee
6 Hie (Hi-de-hi)
8 Keep one's head
10 Amazed
12 Behalf
13 Rover
14 Bath
15 Quit
17 Alert
19 Embody
21 Dancer
23 Kindergarten
24 Rho
25 Thy
26 Sent

Down:
2 Inexact
3 Hopper
4 Deny
5 Easter
6 Hyena
7 End of story
9 Lawbreaker
11 Dolly
12 Beard
16 Unclean
17 Advent
18 Taurus
20 Bingo
22 Ugly

Solutions 155–156

155

Across:		Down:	
1	Antic	2	Natal
4	Witty (Antiquity)	3	Illicit
10	Patella	5	Irate
11	Adder	6	Tadpole
12	Relic	7	Sport
13	Onerous	8	Canoe
15	Idea	9	Grasp
17	Crate	14	Name
19	Mower	16	Debt
22	Beef	18	Remnant
25	Compete	20	Offence
27	Felon	21	Ocean
29	Aware	23	Eerie
30	Ignoble	24	Inter
31	State	26	Eject
32	Realm	28	Label

156

Across:		Down:	
1	Core	2	Ocean
4	Pew	3	Ethical
6	Lent (Corpulent)	4	Pylon
8	Lethal	5	Warfare
9	Reduce	6	Ladle
10	Anaconda	7	Nuclear
11	Epee	10	Asp
12	Parliamentary	13	Abridge
17	Arid	14	Advance
19	Vigilant	15	Tillage
22	Adjoin	16	Yet
23	Eraser	18	Droll
24	Real	20	Greed
25	End	21	Niece
26	Ever		

Solutions 157–158

157

Across:
1 High
4 Doubt (Hideout)
8 Pedigree
9 Ring
10 Spam
11 Old Glory
12 Craven
14 Poodle
16 Reprisal
19 Pour
20 Sore
21 Lethargy
22 Haydn
23 Sikh

Down:
2 Idiom
3 Harpoon
4 Dread
5 Utrillo
6 Tenor
7 Pepper
13 Variety
14 Pilates
15 Lounge
17 Epoch
18 Salon
19 Prank

158

Across:
1 Why
3 Tart
5 Lain (White Hart Lane)
8 Stampede
10 Team
11 Tar
13 Olden
14 Tottenham
16 One
17 Eat
19 Tolerance
21 Ample
22 Kit
24 Away
25 Yuletide
26 Keep
27 Eyed
28 Nod

Down:
1 West
2 Year
3 Typesetter
4 Radish
6 Aberdeen
7 Nominate
9 Talon
12 Comprehend
14 Tomahawk
15 Template
18 Acrid
20 Luxury
22 Kiln
23 Tend

Solutions 159–160

159

Across:

1 Undies
4 Hirer
8 Balls (Undesirables)
9 Angelic
10 Agitate
11 Hype
12 Lap
14 Idle
15 Room
18 Dot
21 Cute
23 Inveigh
25 Recital
26 Deter
27 Dated
28 Credit

Down:

1 Upbeat
2 Dallied
3 Ensnared
4 High
5 Rally
6 Riches
7 Gavel
13 Provider
16 Omitted
17 Scared
19 Title
20 Thirst
22 Tacit
24 Stud

160

Across:

1 Hoar
3 Sunk
9 Heart (Horse and cart)
10 Inebriate
11 Droop
12 Hoi polloi
15 Elated
17 Defeat
19 Plaintiff
21 Cargo
23 Supervise
24 Siege
25 Dusk
26 Pews

Down:

1 Heighten
2 American
4 Usable
5 Khedive
6 Halo
7 Stop
8 Brio
13 Definite
14 Stiffens
16 Exposed
18 Campus
20 Nero
21 Cosh
22 Reek

Solutions 161–162

161

Across:
- **1** War
- **3** Chew
- **5** Hill (What you will)
- **8** Saturate
- **10** Damp
- **11** Hue
- **13** Alibi
- **14** Misdirect
- **16** Ate
- **17** Ere
- **19** Oppressed
- **21** Adieu
- **22** Ban
- **24** Deep
- **25** Immobile
- **26** Rots
- **27** Glad
- **28** Set

Down:
- **1** Wash
- **2** Rite
- **3** Circuitous
- **4** Entice
- **6** Imagines
- **7** Lopsided
- **9** Audit
- **12** Fatherhood
- **14** Marauder
- **15** Sediment
- **18** Regal
- **20** Primal
- **22** Bias
- **23** Neat

162

Across:
- **1** Tusk
- **4** Canny (Tuscany)
- **8** Jettison
- **9** Mien
- **10** Spur
- **11** Rhapsody
- **12** Fennel
- **14** Gasket
- **16** Quantity
- **19** Espy
- **20** Zeal
- **21** Precinct
- **22** Dishy
- **23** Drab

Down:
- **2** Utter
- **3** Kestrel
- **4** Conga
- **5** Nemesis
- **6** Yield
- **7** Weepie
- **13** Nonplus
- **14** Gwynedd
- **15** Expect
- **17** Upend
- **18** Imply
- **19** Evita

Solutions 163–164

163

Across:
1 Force
4 Tall (Forestall)
8 Showman
9 Deuce
10 Sheen
11 Clement
13 Brandy
15 Watson
17 Prefabs
20 Repel
22 Serve
23 Imagery
24 Rake
25 Ether

Down:
1 Fuses
2 Rio de Janeiro
3 Ermined
4 Tonic
5 Ledge
6 Queen's speech
7 Sexton
12 Law
13 Bypass
14 Yob
16 Acreage
18 Arena
19 Seize
21 Layer

164

Across:
1 Gnaw
3 Tickle (Nautical)
9 Liqueur
10 Cheer
11 Ski
12 Pneumatic
13 Trench
14 Jerome
16 Avalanche
19 Sad
21 Expel
22 Viceroy
23 Escudo
24 Kern

Down:
1 Gales
2 Acquire
4 Incompetence
5 Knelt
6 Earache
7 Bespectacled
8 Free
13 Trapeze
15 Observe
17 Aspic
18 Cove
20 Doyen

Solutions 165–166

165

Across:		Down:	
1	Meatier	1	Mobile
8	Wrights (Meteorites)	2	Animal
9	Brief	3	Infrared
10	Renascent	4	Rwanda
11	Lea	5	Zips
12	Larva	6	Cheeky
13	Style	7	Tsetse
14	Squid	13	Saucepan
16	Exult	14	Savage
19	Rye	15	Urging
20	Vegetable	16	Embalm
22	Picky	17	Tracer
23	Genteel	18	Jekyll
24	Mineral	21	Tree

166

Across:		Down:	
1	Fought	1	Fillip
4	Knocks (Fort Knox)	2	Goad
7	Marigolds	3	Tailor
9	Laud	4	Knotty
10	Sore	5	Odds
11	Forth	6	Squeak
13	Pauper	7	Mutuality
14	Yorick	8	Sovietise
15	Pallor	11	Felon
17	Editor	12	Horde
19	Norse	15	Planks
20	Auto	16	Rocket
22	Esau	17	Esther
23	Yorkshire	18	Router
24	Sorest	21	Ooze
25	Rector	22	Eric

Solutions 167–168

167

Across:

1 Purser
4 Veer
9 Rants (Perseverance)
10 Clarity
11 Solvent
12 Ideal
13 Ardent
15 Unless
18 Least
20 Censure
23 Deserve
24 Irate
25 Nile
26 Repeat

Down:

1 Paris
2 Rankled
3 Ensue
5 Elation
6 Raise
7 Acute
8 Cycles
13 Allude
14 Natural
16 Educate
17 Octet
19 Arson
21 Naive
22 Eject

168

Across:

1 Rest
4 Tour
8 Rant (Restaurant)
9 Challenge
11 Energy
13 Beacons
15 Dearth
16 Turtle
18 Aboard
20 Pelota
22 Artisan
23 Coerce
25 Tarantula
26 Leek
27 Type
28 Post

Down:

2 Echo
3 Tiller
4 Trench
5 Urgent
6 Narration
7 Stay
10 Ensures
12 Idea
13 Barometer
14 Attract
17 Edam
19 Dreary
20 Pirate
21 Laptop
23 Colt
24 Alas

Solutions 169–170

169

Across:

1 Lassie
4 Chewed (Lassitude)
9 Verve
10 Absence
11 Pig
12 Scent
13 Leisure
15 Peripatetic
19 Pastime
20 Steal
21 Let
22 Oddball
24 Onset
25 Regret
26 Wealth

Down:

1 Lavish
2 Sorceress
3 Inept
5 Hostile
6 Win
7 Diesel
8 Tagliatelle
14 Universal
16 Imitate
17 Uproar
18 Glitch
20 Stone
23 Dig

170

Across:

1 Choose
4 Dame
8 Awning (Tuesday morning)
9 Street
10 Sever
11 Memento
13 Eden
15 Ski
16 Seem
18 Clamour
20 Venue
23 Evince
24 Ragbag
25 Dull
26 Hoarse

Down:

1 Cowherd
2 Opine
3 Saga
5 Airless
6 Exert
7 Ascetic
12 Assured
14 Nominal
17 Emulate
19 Livid
21 Eager
22 Trio

Solutions 171–172

171

Across:

1 Withers
5 Mile (With a smile)
7 Tiara
8 Induce
10 Sing
11 Straddle
13 Afresh
14 Voyage
17 Dictator
19 Daft
21 Scrimp
22 Alibi
23 Calm
24 Lantern

Down:

1 Withstands
2 Trainer
3 Exam
4 Shifty
5 Mediator
6 Lucid
9 Pedestrian
12 Escapism
15 Avarice
16 Gospel
18 Cocoa
20 Main

172

Across:

1 Thus
3 Hoop
9 Reams (The Supremes)
10 Serengeti
11 Nippy
12 Assistant
15 Ignite
17 Brooch
19 Newspaper
21 Amass
23 Intimates
24 Trial
25 Soho
26 Flea

Down:

1 Tasmania
2 Uprising
4 Operas
5 Printer
6 Damp
7 Espy
8 Onus
13 Hospital
14 Charisma
16 Tonsils
18 Switch
20 Puma
21 Ante
22 Avid

Solutions 173–174

173

Across:

4 Halley
5 Butt (Halibut)
7 Wrangle
10 Prank
11 Tempura
12 Egret
14 Statute
15 Price
16 Referee
20 Canal
21 Telling
22 Zinc
23 Patent

Down:

1 Slant
2 Realm
3 Outrage
4 Harp
6 Tinsel
8 Genteel
9 Epithet
10 Pretzel
13 Ersatz
14 Scrawny
17 Relax
18 Elver
19 Knit

174

Across:

1 Core
4 Don
6 Blur (Cordon bleu)
8 Safari
9 Greedy
10 Sentence
11 Dare
12 Precipitation
17 Used
19 Infernal
22 Armada
23 Leaves
24 Meek
25 Yen
26 Note

Down:

2 Orate
3 Elastic
4 Deign
5 Neglect
6 Blend
7 Undergo
10 Sap
13 Reserve
14 Primary
15 Terrain
16 Nil
18 Drank
20 Felon
21 Adept

Solutions 175–176

175

Across:
1 Welled
4 Unman (Well done man!)
8 Ouzel
9 Banquet
10 Enrages
11 Peel
12 Sew
14 Isis
15 Arch
18 Elk
21 Hobo
23 Inkling
25 Trojans
26 Vesta
27 Pixel
28 Brandt

Down:
1 Wooden
2 Lazarus
3 Eulogise
4 Ulna
5 Mouse
6 Nettle
7 Abyss
13 Walkover
16 Crimson
17 Shut up
19 Kiosk
20 Aghast
22 Bronx
24 Fall

176

Across:
1 Track
4 Shun (Traction)
8 Learner
9 Booze
10 Prior
11 Bargain
13 Thirds
15 Lounge
17 Equerry
20 Fosse
22 Rally
23 As a rule
24 Meet
25 Digit

Down:
1 Tulip
2 Avariciously
3 Kindred
4 Shrub
5 Umber
6 Johannesburg
7 Seance
12 Awl
13 Theory
14 Sir
16 Offhand
18 Rhyme
19 Yeast
21 Exeat

Solutions 177–178

177

Across:
1 Common
5 Dear (Commandeer)
8 Stun
9 Protocol
10 Uphill
11 Bright
12 Minesweeper
15 Strand
17 Virago
19 Taciturn
20 Suit
21 Less
22 Spleen

Down:
2 On tap
3 Mansion
4 Nepal
5 Dhoti
6 Another
7 Double
12 Methane
13 Sodium
14 Parasol
16 Adios
17 Venus
18 Gripe

178

Across:
1 Con
3 Tree
5 Boot (Contribute)
8 Lady-love
10 Mesa
11 Ale
13 Hocus
14 Free-rider
16 Amp
17 Age
19 Pedometer
21 Filth
22 Goa
24 Urge
25 Lassoing
26 Glen
27 Zeus
28 Tug

Down:
1 Cola
2 Nude
3 Telegraphy
4 Envied
6 Overcoat
7 Transfer
9 Alarm
12 Thrombosis
14 Far-flung
15 Epilogue
18 Get on
20 Donate
22 Gift
23 Agog

Solutions 179–180

179

Across:

1 Sin
3 Till
5 Late (Scintillate)
8 Abstract
10 Stye
11 Pit
13 Lithe
14 Clientele
16 Hen
17 Dot
19 Tasteless
21 Large
22 Bet
24 Real
25 Pleasure
26 Need
27 Tray
28 Yet

Down:

1 Swap
2 Nest
3 Terminated
4 Locate
6 Altitude
7 Elements
9 Bible
12 Elementary
14 Children
15 Increase
18 Osier
20 Sailor
22 Bury
23 Test

180

Across:

1 Trance
5 Sport (Transport)
9 Arbitrate
10 Sea
11 Cat
12 Blameless
14 Lid
16 Eject
18 Ear
19 Ascertain
21 Gas
22 Ire
23 Manifesto
25 Nasty
26 Willow

Down:

2 Robot
3 Notable
4 Era
5 Sieve
6 Obscene
7 Transgressor
8 Cancellation
13 Arena
15 Duchess
17 Tuneful
20 Rummy
21 Gusto
24 New

Solutions 181–182

181

Across:
1 Matter
5 Doors (Matadors)
9 Occupancy
10 Fop
11 Tea
12 Raconteur
14 Rug
16 Donor
18 Tit
19 Overwhelm
21 Pot
22 Goa
23 Esperanto
25 React
26 Paella

Down:
2 Accra
3 Tapered
4 Run
5 Doyen
6 Offbeat
7 Superstition
8 Costermonger
13 Canoe
15 Grenada
17 Remorse
20 Wheat
21 Panel
24 Pup

182

Across:
1 Nigh
4 Towel (Night owl)
8 Popsicle
9 Real
10 Huge
11 Nitrogen
12 Feisty
14 Ankara
16 Wheatear
19 Tuba
20 Oval
21 Reckless
22 Catch
23 Type

Down:
2 Issue
3 Hockney
4 Treat
5 Warlock
6 Leave
7 Volume
13 Shallot
14 Apricot
15 Robust
17 Havoc
18 Earth
19 Tulip

Solutions 183–184

183

Across:		Down:	
1	Annex	1	Afraid
4	Queues (An excuse)	2	Nudge
9	Radiant	3	X-ray
10	Duped	5	Undulate
11	Idea	6	Umpires
12	Culprit	7	Sedate
13	Irk	8	Stick
14	Spam	13	Imagined
16	Toss	15	Pliable
18	Ape	17	Accuse
20	Cringed	18	Adder
21	Fair	19	Ardent
24	Urban	22	Abide
25	Edifice	23	Cite
26	Emends		
27	Erect		

184

Across:		Down:	
1	Thug	2	Hippies
4	Aim	3	Geckos
6	Sup (The game's up)	4	Alas
8	Spick-and-span	5	Modify
10	Briton	6	Sepia
12	Affair	7	Pen friends
13	Soppy	9	Abstemious
14	Task	11	No-nos
15	Like	12	April
17	Motif	16	Indulge
19	Mantis	17	Mining
21	Lauded	18	Father
23	Once in a while	20	Niche
24	Sue	22	Hang
25	Gag		
26	Rued		

Solutions 185–186

185

Across:
1 Lie
3 Tough
6 Ire (Light a fire)
8 Veils
9 Suspend
10 Thereafter
12 Nap
15 Race
17 Tale
18 Era
22 Refinement
25 Appoint
26 Dense
27 Sex
28 Lorry
29 Lit

Down:
1 Lavatory
2 Evidence
3 Tested
4 Unsafe
5 Hasten
6 Idea
7 Eddy
11 Rat
13 Paternal
14 Sentient
16 Err
19 Aerial
20 Victor
21 Deadly
23 Pass
24 Apex

186

Across:
1 Castor
4 Weigh (Castaway)
8 Merit
9 America
10 Astride
11 Omit
12 Sea
14 Shoe
15 Puff
18 Sit
21 Also
23 Earlier
25 Purpose
26 Ashes
27 Reeds
28 Ghosts

Down:
1 Combat
2 Scratch
3 Outlines
4 Weed
5 Idiom
6 Hearty
7 Fades
13 Approach
16 Flights
17 Hamper
19 Tenet
20 Crisis
22 Spree
24 Jobs

Solutions 187–188

187

Across:

1 Barb
3 Accuse (Barbecues)
9 Reserve
10 Squat
11 Tar
12 Patroller
13 Remiss
14 Joyous
16 Donizetti
19 Elf
21 Allot
22 Granary
23 Tanker
24 Dear

Down:

1 Beret
2 Rostrum
4 Cosmopolitan
5 Usual
6 Extorts
7 Crepe suzette
8 Heat
13 Radiant
15 Overawe
17 Nylon
18 Togo
20 Foyer

188

Across:

1 Force
4 Wearing (Forswearing)
8 Samurai
9 Pique
10 Naomi
11 Shyness
13 Goya
15 Taoism
17 Victim
20 Aden
22 Codeine
24 Jazzy
26 Plaid
27 Miranda
28 Relaxes
29 Solar

Down:

1 Fish-net
2 Romeo
3 Earwigs
4 Whimsy
5 Amply
6 Inquest
7 Geeks
12 Have
14 Oman
16 Oddball
18 Injures
19 Mayfair
21 Dermis
22 Caper
23 Index
25 Zonal

Solutions 189–190

189

Across:
1 Beef
4 Rend
8 Ding (Befriending)
9 Palladium
11 Taurus
13 Chicken
15 Groyne
16 Ramped
18 Nodose
20 Tedium
22 Prouder
23 Mutton
25 Tea kettle
26 Flow
27 Stay
28 Lamb

Down:
2 Exam
3 Filthy
4 Reduce
5 Neuter
6 Disrepair
7 Eggs
10 Managed
12 Ogen
13 Condition
14 In a spot
17 Dump
19 Ernest
20 Turkey
21 Dental
23 Muff
24 Slim

190

Across:
1 Meatier
5 Right (Meteorite)
8 Tepee
9 Cockade
10 Fireman
11 Taper
12 Canard
14 Hansom
17 Pilot
19 Hogwash
22 Curling
23 Vapid
24 Tesla
25 Nonplus

Down:
1 Motif
2 Aspirin
3 Ileum
4 Recant
5 Ricotta
6 Grasp
7 Theorem
12 Copycat
13 Retsina
15 Scalpel
16 Shogun
18 Lures
20 Given
21 Hades

Solutions 191–192

191

Across:

1 Hiss
4 Panic (Hispanic)
8 Brethren
9 Norm
10 Dear
11 Inaction
12 Statue
14 Appear
16 Abundant
19 Dire
20 Poor
21 Required
22 Humid
23 Ewer

Down:

2 Inter
3 Servile
4 Panda
5 Non-stop
6 Cargo
7 Arrest
13 Tantrum
14 Antique
15 Agreed
17 Booth
18 Acrid
19 Drive

192

Across:

1 Pig
3 Smite
6 Fly (Pigs might fly)
8 Nanny
9 Farrier
10 Earthquake
12 Ale
15 Club
17 Know
18 Sad
22 Gymnastics
25 Corsair
26 Cacti
27 Old
28 Obese
29 Era

Down:

1 Pungency
2 Generous
3 Scythe
4 Influx
5 Eureka
6 Fair
7 Yarn
11 Elk
13 Encircle
14 Swastika
16 Bag
19 Dynamo
20 Untrue
21 Psyche
23 Echo
24 Prod

Solutions 193–194

193

Across:

1	Lynn
4	Con
6	Sin (Lincoln's Inn)
8	Illustration
10	Rascal
12	Glitch
13	Tokay
14	Fine
15	Tall
17	Greet
19	Tawdry
21	Listen
23	Brilliantine
24	Ewe
25	Ebb
26	Peak

Down:

2	Yeltsin
3	Nougat
4	Cats
5	Nearly
6	Swift
7	Nonchalant
9	Profitable
11	Lorry
12	Gavel
16	Antenna
17	Grille
18	Tiptop
20	Write
22	Barb

194

Across:

7	Cannes
8	Tartar (Cantata)
10	Limpopo
11	Baize
12	Cull
13	Vixen
17	Quilt
18	Area
22	Fling
23	Tribute
24	Anchor
25	Lethal

Down:

1	Schlock
2	Anomaly
3	Melon
4	Warbler
5	Stain
6	Preen
9	Joviality
14	Dungeon
15	Drought
16	Gazelle
19	Offal
20	Ditch
21	Widen

Solutions 195–196

195

Across:		Down:	
1	Phase	1	Picks
4	Thief	2	Ail
8	Axe (Face the facts)	3	Embrace
9	Celebrities	4	Tribes
10	Sausage	5	Idiot
12	Teeth	6	Fastening
13	Redeem	7	Benches
14	Ladies	11	Underling
17	Marks	13	Romance
19	Sponged	15	Apostle
21	Inscrutable	16	Astray
23	Can	18	Sushi
24	Grimy	20	Dread
25	Erred	22	Bar

196

Across:		Down:	
1	Suitor	1	Settlement
4	Farmer (Suit of armour)	2	Irreverent
7	Turnpike	3	Opposite
9	Netting	4	Flee
12	Loves	5	Root
13	Inept	6	Even
15	Merit	8	Knee
16	Upend	10	Intertwine
17	Eager	11	Guidelines
19	Natal	14	Turncoat
20	Titular	18	Gore
24	Demotion	21	Itch
25	Charge	22	User
26	Stress	23	Adze

Solutions 197–198

197

Across:
1 Tsar
5 Dean (Sardine)
7 Uruguay
8 Biarritz
10 Abet
12 Spud
14 Aperture
16 Hospital
17 Cute
18 Neon
19 Vagrancy
22 Stetson
23 Toss
24 Teak

Down:
1 Tomb
2 Ruhr
3 Jubilant
4 Quiz
5 Dynastic
6 Newt
9 Improve
11 Erratic
13 Dopiness
15 Eulogise
18 Next
19 View
20 Aunt
21 Yolk

198

Across:
1 Sigh
4 Bus
6 Pace (Cyberspace)
8 Savage
9 Outset
10 Teetotal
11 Hard
12 Consternation
17 Dirt
19 Prospect
22 Simple
23 Exceed
24 Nerd
25 See
26 Loop

Down:
2 Irate
3 Hearths
4 Bleat
5 Swollen
6 Pitch
7 Cheerio
10 Tic
13 Orifice
14 Express
15 Topical
16 Net
18 Tepid
20 Obese
21 Credo

Solutions 199–200

199

Across:

1	Piquet
4	Number (Pick a number)
7	Chitchat
9	New York
12	Limbs
13	Evens
15	Assam
16	Chile
17	Enoch
18	Erase
19	Yardarm
23	Escaping
24	Friend
25	Launch

Down:

1	Peculiarly
2	Quizmaster
3	Excuse me
4	Note
5	Many
6	Ever
8	Anterooms
10	Obligation
11	Knee-length
14	Schemata
20	Ajar
21	Dame
22	Read

200

Across:

1	Ketchup
5	Later (Catch up later)
8	Pixel
9	Travail
10	Aquatic
11	Dunce
12	Breezy
14	Browse
17	Epsom
19	Offhand
22	Amusing
23	Logic
24	Sands
25	Respect

Down:

1	Kappa
2	Texture
3	Holst
4	Putsch
5	Leander
6	Train
7	Relieve
12	Bye-laws
13	Zombies
15	Wrangle
16	Jogger
18	Spurn
20	Files
21	Ducat

Solutions 201–202

201

Across:

1 Cell
4 Frays
8 In flower (Self-raising flour)
9 Salt
10 Hint
11 Underdog
12 Knight
14 Banish
16 Amundsen
19 Fury
20 Arch
21 Breather
22 Lemur
23 Sway

Down:

2 Eclat
3 Lawsuit
4 Fired
5 Also-ran
6 Salvo
7 Ensign
13 Gingham
14 Bonkers
15 Screed
17 Morel
18 Sober
19 Fatwa

202

Across:

1 Haul
4 Day
6 Hand
8 Oliver
9 Knight (All day and all of the night)
10 Angriest
11 Typo
12 Hard-luck story
17 Just
19 Laburnum
22 Offcut
23 Kaolin
24 Writ
25 Hod
26 Lynx

Down:

2 All in
3 Levered
4 Dirge
5 Yakutsk
6 Hoist
7 No-hoper
10 Ash
13 Aquifer
14 Unlatch
15 Turmoil
16 Yam
18 Tacit
20 Baked
21 Union

Solutions 203–204

203

Across:		Down:	
1	Haughty	1	Hocus-pocus
5	Cult	2	Utopian
7	Chore (Horticulture)	3	Heed
8	Allude	4	Yearly
10	Slim	5	Celerity
11	Clarinet	6	Laden
13	Ornate	9	Stationery
14	Strict	12	Studious
17	Unending	15	Illegal
19	Also	16	Indeed
21	Cajole	18	Erase
22	Argue	20	Lass
23	Lees		
24	Display		

204

Across:		Down:	
1	Mute	2	Used
4	Till	3	Eleven
8	Late (Mutilate)	4	Torpid
9	Celebrate	5	Letter
11	Taurus	6	Barrister
13	Delibes	7	Mess
15	Pernod	10	Easeful
16	Reason	12	Opus
18	Simmer	13	Dramatist
20	Rubens	14	Lozenge
22	Nebular	17	Nest
23	Potage	19	Reeled
25	Elaborate	20	Rubber
26	Cost	21	Barrel
27	Oder	23	Pact
28	Link	24	Stun

Solutions 205–206

205

Across:

1 Pecan
4 Chews (Pick and choose)
10 Setting
11 Meant
12 Drama
13 Punched
15 Lots
17 Grasp
19 Entry
22 Ease
25 Content
27 Ruler
29 Aging
30 Amounts
31 Agree
32 Ascot

Down:

2 Extra
3 Animals
5 Human
6 Weather
7 Aside
8 Egypt
9 Study
14 Uses
16 Open
18 Running
20 Nervous
21 Ocean
23 Atlas
24 Press
26 Eagle
28 Lingo

206

Across:

1 Force
4 Where (Forswear)
8 Thunder
9 Uncle
10 Audrey Hepburn
11 Aghast
12 Harass
15 Future perfect
18 Climb
19 Tangent
20 Tally
21 Extol

Down:

1 Fatwa
2 Round the twist
3 Endless
4 Worthy
5 Equip
6 Encouragement
7 Tennis
11 Affect
13 Arrange
14 Apathy
16 Rebel
17 Total

Solutions 207–208

207

Across:

1 Act
3 Jaw
5 Rage (Act your age)
7 Quake
8 Issued
10 Iris
11 Charisma
13 Sagged
14 Fierce
17 Explicit
19 Cure
21 Oracle
22 Roots
23 Cede
24 Yet
25 Say

Down:

1 Acquiesced
2 Trading
3 Jeer
4 Weight
5 Restrain
6 Guess
9 Carelessly
12 Mediocre
15 Raucous
16 Timely
18 Purge
20 Grit

208

Across:

1 Freak
4 Hunt
7 Tree (Free country)
8 Outgoing
9 Continent
10 Dye
12 Snoops
14 Hearts
16 Eye
18 Enigmatic
21 Musician
22 Cite
23 Shut
24 Rider

Down:

1 Forlorn
2 Exertion
3 Known
4 Hood
5 Nanny
6 Stench
11 Balanced
13 Sunlit
15 Twitter
17 Youth
19 Goner
20 Diet

Solutions 209–210

209

Across:

1 Par
3 Rim
5 Arch (Paris Match)
7 Squad
8 Setter
10 Evil
11 Garrison
13 Seemed
14 Deduce
17 Outdated
19 Cure
21 Imbibe
22 Taunt
23 Stay
24 Top
25 Lad

Down:

1 Possession
2 Routine
3 Rude
4 Mislay
5 Attorney
6 Chefs
9 Interested
12 Tenacity
15 Unusual
16 Deceit
18 Tempt
20 Step

210

Across:

1 Caw
3 Beat
5 Rows
8 Suppress (Corby Trouser Press)
10 Deep
11 Ere
13 Caste
14 Paso doble
16 Ink
17 Opt
19 Insincere
21 Solar
22 Imp
24 Nuts
25 Transfer
26 Rile
27 Gear
28 Yum

Down:

1 Case
2 Wipe
3 Barbed wire
4 Absorb
6 Overshoe
7 Septette
9 Urban
12 Ocean liner
14 Pilsener
15 Skeletal
18 Prime
20 Swerve
22 Iffy
23 Prom

Solutions 211–212

211

Across:

1	Seoul
4	Annoyed (Solenoid)
8	Ult
9	Moa
10	Onset
11	Loren
12	Azimuth
15	Ante
17	Retire
19	Shield
22	Site
24	Sextets
26	Iambi
28	Irate
30	Age
31	Job
32	Recital
33	Spree

Down:

1	Squalor
2	Otter
3	Laminar
4	Ararat
5	Naomi
6	Yes
7	Ditch
13	Zest
14	Ure
16	Nest
18	Tax
20	Heifers
21	Dribble
23	Israel
24	Skier
25	Event
27	Major
29	Arc

212

Across:

1	Gnus
3	Swarthy (Newsworthy)
8	Jumper
9	Empire
10	Yearbook
11	Draw
12	Gossip
15	Decade
17	Quit
19	Off-piste
22	Mexico
23	Renown
24	Stiffen
25	Pier

Down:

1	Gauze
2	Umpires
4	Wrecked
5	Rapid
6	Harvard
7	Ergo
13	Opulent
14	Provoke
16	Chianti
18	Thief
20	Fern
21	Tower

Solutions 213–214

213

Across:		Down:	
1	Prick	1	Placard
4	Leap	2	Irritability
8	Air (Prickly pear)	3	Kiwi
9	Wasteland	4	Losing
10	Alto	5	Adequate
11	Unbuckle	6	Jack-in-the-box
12	Erg	7	Adze
13	Dublin	11	Urn
14	Stench	12	Einstein
16	Foe	14	Sod
17	Molested	15	Hansard
18	Shin	16	Ferret
20	Cathedral	17	Mock
21	Bra	19	Slav
22	Gnat		
23	Vexed		

214

Across:		Down:	
1	Fall	2	Adieu
4	Tit	3	Lift-off
6	Ours (Fawlty Towers)	4	Terry
8	Pilfer	5	Tugboat
9	Gatsby	6	On tap
10	Autogyro	7	Rubella
11	Poly	10	Aid
12	Dysfunctional	13	Yuckier
17	Scab	14	Nostrum
19	Skittish	15	Outgrow
22	Kisser	16	Lah
23	Scribe	18	Basil
24	Oral	20	Ibsen
25	Man	21	Sibyl
26	Well		

Solutions 215–216

215

Across:		Down:	
1	Penny	2	Erase
4	Tense (Penitence)	3	Naughty
10	Measure	5	Erato
11	Allow	6	Sultana
12	Leech	7	Ample
13	Isolate	8	Eerie
15	Trek	9	Owner
17	Tokyo	14	Skid
19	Ideal	16	Role
22	Lady	18	Opulent
25	Blunder	20	Dynasty
27	Naval	21	Abhor
29	Ocean	23	Arson
30	Observe	24	Alien
31	Strew	26	Dense
32	Nylon	28	Virgo

216

Across:		Down:	
1	Maker	1	Measure
4	Miss	2	Keepsake
7	Take (Make a mistake)	3	Ruler
8	Language	4	Maul
9	Subscribe	5	Sight
10	Sty	6	Enable
12	Weaken	11	Abnormal
14	Embody	13	Nearly
16	Act	15	Dentist
18	Paramount	17	Comma
21	Umbrella	19	Amass
22	Maim	20	Aria
23	Gala		
24	Split		

Solutions 217–218

217

Across:
1 Quay
4 Whole (Keyhole)
8 Follower
9 Kite
10 Pact
11 Inherent
12 Sarong
14 Pretty
16 Trifling
19 Sane
20 Turn
21 Peaceful
22 Enemy
23 Tiny

Down:
2 Unlit
3 Yawning
4 Worth
5 Oak tree
6 Eaten
7 Sonata
13 Offence
14 Pageant
15 Tongue
17 Route
18 Imply
19 Stern

218

Across:
1 Mall
4 Tease (Maltese)
8 Collapse
9 Duel
10 Hazy
11 Intimate
12 Oil rig
14 Arnhem
16 Quick-fix
19 View
20 Just
21 Ideology
22 Prawn
23 Yeti

Down:
2 Alley
3 Lapwing
4 Trent
5 Abdomen
6 Elect
7 Somali
13 Ricotta
14 Anxiety
15 Energy
17 Usurp
18 Feign
19 Valet

Solutions 219–220

219

Across:

1 May
3 Cures
6 Kin
8 Crawl (Make your skin crawl)
9 Warrior
10 Ornamental
12 Man
15 Etna
17 Pork
18 Gnu
22 Transition
25 Madeira
26 Range
27 Ray
28 Greed
29 Lip

Down:

1 Microbes
2 Yearning
3 Column
4 Rowing
5 Stream
6 Knit
7 Nary
11 Lap
13 Notional
14 Skin-deep
16 Ant
19 Urging
20 Unsafe
21 Tiered
23 Emir
24 Edgy

220

Across:

1 Windsor
5 Furze (Windsurfers)
8 Vital
9 Collide
10 Surreal
11 Obese
12 Collar
14 Attest
17 Found
19 Tragedy
22 Exhibit
23 Eagle
24 Spree
25 Hoarded

Down:

1 Wives
2 Natural
3 Solve
4 Recall
5 Fall out
6 Raise
7 Everest
12 Coffers
13 Audible
15 Emerged
16 Stitch
18 Usher
20 Arena
21 Yield

Solutions 221–222

221

Across:
4 Matter
5 Door (Matador)
7 Quarter
10 Large
11 Erratic
12 Ghoul
14 Panache
15 Midas
16 Po-faced
20 Gabon
21 Narrate
22 Oust
23 Craven

Down:
1 Store
2 Leper
3 Gouache
4 Maul
6 Ragout
8 Treason
9 Ramadan
10 Lighter
13 Virago
14 Papoose
17 Cadre
18 Drove
19 Stun

222

Across:
1 Serve
4 Aunties (Cervantes)
8 Run
9 Pig
10 Bulge
11 Ashen
12 Elegant
15 Sore
17 Spoken
19 Ardent
22 Code
24 Barrier
26 Creed
28 Mania
30 Apt
31 Urn
32 Supreme
33 Lulls

Down:
1 Surpass
2 Ranch
3 Expense
4 Angler
5 Noble
6 Ill
7 Sweet
13 Lead
14 Ale
16 Once
18 Oar
20 Recital
21 Tidings
23 Ornate
24 Bumps
25 Image
27 Equal
29 Nap

Solutions 223–224

223

Across:

1	Income
4	Pleat (Incomplete)
8	Banjo
9	Refugee
10	Baubles
11	Vest
12	Tam
14	Wren
15	Elan
18	Day
21	Rake
23	Acreage
25	Explain
26	Chimp
27	Drain
28	Plague

Down:

1	Imbibe
2	Conquer
3	Moorland
4	Puff
5	Eagle
6	Twenty
7	Frost
13	Metrical
16	Amazing
17	Friend
19	Yawns
20	Temple
22	Kappa
24	Dawn

224

Across:

1	Thyme
5	Peace (Timepiece)
8	Lento
9	Jeans
10	Inquorate
11	Awn
12	Stonewaller
15	Leprechauns
19	Air
20	Flattered
22	Awoke
23	Nylon
24	Exalt
25	Terse

Down:

1	Taj Mahal
2	Yearns
3	Elsinore
4	Unique
5	Polo
6	Assail
7	Edge
13	Abundant
14	Retrieve
16	Piazza
17	Herald
18	Savour
20	Fame
21	Tent

Solutions 225–226

225

Across:

1 Nicker
5 Ragu
8 Wore (Nicaragua)
9 Flippant
10 Eyelet
11 The Who
12 Pandemonium
15 Gateau
17 Mahler (Guatemala)
19 Retainer
20 Loom
21 Cost
22 Eureka (Costa Rica)

Down:

2 Ivory
3 Kremlin
4 Refit
5 Rupee
6 Gingham
7 Bistro
12 Placebo
13 Equine
14 Inhaler
16 Exact
17 Morse
18 E-book

226

Across:

1 Hay
3 Press
6 Tow (Hey presto)
8 Wound
9 Bolster
10 High and dry
12 Yak
15 Rusk
17 Pelt
18 Teg
22 Gamekeeper
25 Trachea
26 Latch
27 Wit
28 Relax
29 Tad

Down:

1 Hawthorn
2 Youngest
3 Pedlar
4 Embody
5 Salary
6 Tutu
7 Work
11 Yap
13 Keep at it
14 Starched
16 Keg
19 Gather
20 Detail
21 Reflex
23 Stew
24 Fact

Solutions 227–228

227

Across:

1 Super
4 Intend (Superintend)
9 Dense
10 Optimum
11 Entreat
12 Cling
14 Ewe
15 Cat
16 Gem
18 Cap
21 Clear
22 Lighter
23 Adamant
25 Excel
26 Larder
27 Delay

Down:

1 Sudden
2 Penetrate
3 Reeled
5 Notice
6 Elm
7 Damage
8 Contemplate
13 Identical
17 Scrawl
18 Create
19 Agreed
20 Trilby
24 Air

228

Across:

1 Bridle
4 Sweet (Bridal suite)
8 Axiom
9 Absence
10 Chianti
11 Pier
12 Dad
14 Glad
15 Apex
18 Era
21 Easy
23 Traipse
25 Termini
26 Annoy
27 Theft
28 Cereal

Down:

1 Branch
2 Initial
3 Lemonade
4 Sash
5 Ennui
6 Theory
7 Rapid
13 Database
16 Expense
17 Sextet
19 Attic
20 Jekyll
22 Serve
24 Gift

Solutions 229–230

229

Across:		Down:	
1	Mill	2	Irate
4	War	3	Lectern
6	Quay (Milwaukee)	4	Wilde
8	Rascal	5	Rosette
9	Smooth	6	Quota
10	Vehement	7	Antonio
11	Anne	10	Vet
12	Transgression	13	Retract
17	Stag	14	Goulash
19	Upheaval	15	Shallow
22	Paella	16	Nil
23	Allege	18	Gully
24	Stay	20	Heart
25	Hut	21	Anger
26	Wary		

230

Across:		Down:	
1	Cattle	2	Ample
5	Anne (Catalan)	3	Tonight
8	Spin	4	Elbow
9	Bankrupt	5	Arrow
10	Gewgaw	6	Neptune
11	Lawful	7	Angler
12	Catastrophe	12	Cyclone
15	Scrawl	13	Seller
17	Danube	14	Pennant
19	Sombrero	16	Abbey
20	Ajar	17	Droll
21	Levy	18	Brawn
22	Litany		

Solutions 231–232

231

Across:

1 Hissed
5 Tree
8 Onyx (Histrionics)
9 Normally
10 Arcade
11 Exempt
12 Make believe
15 Isobar
17 Ticker
19 Narrates
20 Acts
21 Bald
22 Sombre

Down:

2 Inner
3 Six-pack
4 Dance
5 Trace
6 Eclipse
7 Ordeal
12 Mascara
13 Berate
14 Exclaim
16 Bored
17 Tasks
18 Enter

232

Across:

1 Clash
4 Nick
8 Off (Kalashnikov)
9 Stagnated
10 Pact
11 Peerless
12 Pan
13 Ruined
14 Frolic
16 May
17 Consider
18 Scar
20 Entourage
21 Ape
22 Cede
23 Bleat

Down:

1 Chopper
2 Affectionate
3 Hose
4 Neaten
5 Contrary
6 Steeplechase
7 Odes
11 Pad
12 Pedicure
14 Far
15 Current
16 Menace
17 Crew
19 Kerb

Solutions 233–234

233

Across:

1 Lay
3 Safe
5 Hair (Laissez-faire)
8 Purveyor
10 Less
11 End
13 Opted
14 Remainder
16 Ode
17 Ran
19 Incorrect
21 Alias
22 Woe
24 Tact
25 Standard
26 Chew
27 Fear
28 Yet

Down:

1 Lope
2 Yard
3 Scepticism
4 Florid
6 Aperture
7 Resident
9 Unwed
12 Forerunner
14 Romantic
15 Mediocre
18 Actor
20 Clothe
22 Wary
23 Edit

234

Across:

1 Boo
3 Beep
5 Rise (Booby prize)
8 Occasion
10 Emus
11 Toe
13 Rodeo
14 Conceited
16 One
17 Sac
19 Lorgnette
21 Chafe
22 End
24 Ruin
25 Reminder
26 Omen
27 Cloy
28 Elm

Down:

1 Boot
2 Once
3 Bestseller
4 Egoist
6 Immodest
7 Ensconce
9 Colon
12 Ordinarily
14 Concerto
15 Negative
18 Atone
20 Reveal
22 Edge
23 Drum

Solutions 235–236

235

Across:
1 Conned
4 Owning (Condoning)
7 Evacuate
9 Angelus
12 Troop
13 Panic
15 Elite
16 Eager
17 Desks
18 Spiky
19 Tenable
23 Adroitly
24 Jumble
25 Placid

Down:
1 Chew the fat
2 Neapolitan
3 Equipped
4 Oxen
5 Nave
6 Non-U
8 Tarnished
10 Linguistic
11 Starry-eyed
14 Cesspool
20 Ecru
21 Arab
22 Laze

236

Across:
1 Parr
3 Tickles (Particles)
8 Vandal
9 Animus
10 Stiletto
11 Elba
12 Jungle
15 Disney
17 Wasp
19 Helsinki
22 Milieu
23 Zephyr
24 Amnesty
25 Beck

Down:
1 Plant
2 Red flag
4 In a word
5 Knife
6 Equable
7 Plot
13 Uranium
14 Exhaust
16 Stipple
18 Pride
20 Lazy
21 Kayak

Solutions 237–238

237

Across:

1 Peak
4 Unease (Pekingese)
8 Supplant
9 Duck
10 Ludo
11 Unwind
13 Dundee
16 Modem
17 Obese
19 Begone
22 Mirror
24 Worm
25 Abed
26 Scrutiny
27 Usurer
28 Oche

Down:

2 Explode
3 Klaxon
4 Untrue
5 Endow
6 Second string
7 Cumulonimbus
12 Neon
14 Umbo
15 Dog
18 Bewitch
20 Eraser
21 Overdo
23 Radar

238

Across:

1 Furs
3 Twirled
7 Wore (First World War)
8 Epee
9 Auditor
10 Galley
13 Polly
14 Oust
16 Tanker
18 Thatch
20 Memo
21 Somme
22 Wipers
25 Turbine
26 Gaga
27 Wake
28 Passion
29 Dale

Down:

1 Freight
2 Swell
3 Teak
4 In-depth
5 Little toe
6 Derby
11 Landmarks
12 Yore
15 Stow
17 Emeriti
19 Hostage
21 Set-up
23 Paged
24 Hewn

Solutions 239–240

239

Across:

1 Naps
4 Sacks (Knapsacks)
8 Accident
9 Pelt
10 Sign
11 Donation
12 Geyser
14 Dulcet
16 Complete
19 Duty
20 Oboe
21 Answered
22 Title
23 Rule

Down:

2 Alien
3 Slender
4 Satan
5 Capital
6 Salvo
7 Active
13 Sapient
14 Dresser
15 Esteem
17 Orbit
18 Erase
19 Dwell

240

Across:

1 Morphia
5 Money (More for your money)
8 Rider
9 Aspirin
10 Terrorise
12 Ace
13 Zapata
14 Choirs
17 Son
18 Permanent
20 Frantic
21 Tongs
23 Lotto
24 Sincere

Down:

1 Merit
2 Rod
3 Hire out
4 Adagio
5 Maple
6 Narrative
7 Yankees
11 Repentant
13 Zestful
15 Hearten
16 Fracas
18 Patio
19 Taste
22 Nee

Solutions 241–242

241

Across:

4 Singer
5 Poor (Singapore)
7 In vogue
10 Arise
11 Western
12 Melee
14 Burnley
15 Maori
16 Inhabit
20 Bilge
21 Nearest
22 Hunk
23 Loathe

Down:

1 Endow
2 Venus
3 Journey
4 Sane
6 Rasher
8 Genuine
9 Etonian
10 Armenia
13 Lavish
14 Brigand
17 Besom
18 Trite
19 Isle

242

Across:

1 Melon
4 Colly (Melancholy)
10 Dressed
11 Grace
12 Utter
13 Lunches
15 Vets
17 Honey
19 Entry
22 Ease
25 Whitest
27 Rebel
29 Lotus
30 Ironing
31 Oddly
32 Usher

Down:

2 Event
3 Observe
5 Organ
6 Leather
7 Odour
8 Adult
9 Dense
14 Uses
16 Eyes
18 Omitted
20 Nervous
21 Dwell
23 Attic
24 Flags
26 Easel
28 Bribe

Solutions 243–244

243

Across:

1 May
3 Kiss
5 Tory (Make history)
8 Straight
10 Etna
11 Tot
13 Let in
14 Scintilla
16 Ohm
17 Inn
19 Off-the-peg
21 Credo
22 Rue
24 Ruin
25 Pitiless
26 Rile
27 Pelt
28 Lay

Down:

1 Mist
2 Yurt
3 Knighthood
4 School
6 Outstrip
7 Yearning
9 Touch
12 Flashpoint
14 Sorcerer
15 Imperial
18 Nexus
20 Feline
22 Real
23 Espy

244

Across:

1 Guess
5 Douse (Guest-house)
8 Abhor
9 Motel
10 Itsy-bitsy
11 Tea
12 Play on words
15 Non sequitur
19 Ego
20 Successor
22 Learn
23 Torso
24 Mores
25 Owner

Down:

1 Gumption
2 Entrap
3 Salivate
4 Physio
5 Drab
6 Ulster
7 Easy
13 Waterloo
14 Schooner
16 Nectar
17 Unsure
18 Remain
20 Sham
21 Eats

Solutions 245–246

245

Across:
1 Itch
4 Cox
6 Psi
9 Coe (Hitchcock's Psycho)
10 Donor
11 Often
12 Pas de deux
15 Condensed milk
19 Press stud
21 Photo
22 Usher
24 Uzi
25 Lie
26 Dye
27 Ewer

Down:
2 Treason
3 Hedge
4 Con
5 Xeroxed
6 Paste
7 Iron
8 Icepack
13 Ensue
14 Skid lid
16 Expound
17 Intrude
18 Rouse
20 Spree
21 Pall
23 Hoe

246

Across:
1 Overran
5 Doubt (Over and out)
8 Equip
9 Dnieper
10 Appraisal
12 Pie
13 Finale
14 Mullet
17 Eta
18 Edinburgh
20 Deposit
21 Amber
23 Dream
24 Endorse

Down:
1 Opera
2 Emu
3 Raphael
4 Nudist
5 Drill
6 Unpopular
7 Torment
11 Pineapple
13 Fielded
15 Upbraid
16 Little
18 Epsom
19 Horde
22 Bar

Solutions 247–248

247

Across:
1 Crew
5 Zing (Cruising)
7 Rossini
8 Prophesy
10 Buff
12 Onus
14 Scabbard
16 Shoulder
17 Envy
18 Bred
19 Jodhpurs
22 Oracles
23 Kiln
24 Taxi

Down:
1 Clap
2 Wrap
3 Aspersed
4 City
5 Zimbabwe
6 Golf
9 Rancher
11 Forever
13 Squadron
15 Airedale
18 Bunk
19 Joan
20 Post
21 Sari

248

Across:
1 Panned
4 Aura (Pandora)
8 Trivia
9 Ratify
10 Quilt
11 Seville
13 Myth
15 Cue
16 Daft
18 Studied
20 Acute
23 Sarong
24 Klaxon
25 Lake
26 Sports

Down:
1 Perjury
2 Novel
3 Elan
5 Untried
6 Awful
7 Breezes
12 Acreage
14 Haddock
17 Fatuous
19 Trail
21 Chair
22 Skip

Solutions 249–250

249

Across:

1 How
3 Strained (House-trained)
9 Tutor
10 Bristol
11 Hog
13 Maelstrom
14 Shifty
16 Fedora
18 Pilferage
20 Sob
22 Admiral
23 Order
25 Outsmart
26 Pal

Down:

1 Hitch
2 Wit
4 Tablet
5 At issue
6 Notorious
7 Dilemma
8 Grim
12 Guillemot
14 Soprano
15 Theorem
17 Sailor
19 Eros
21 Beryl
24 Dip

250

Across:

1 Commerce
8 Shawls (Commercials)
9 Advert
10 Roughest
11 Freeze
13 Nightcap
17 Metaphor
20 Airbag
23 Jumbo jet
25 Influx
26 Unison
27 King-size

Down:

2 Order
3 My eye
4 Retrench
5 Esau
6 Cachet
7 Plasma
11 Firm
12 Exit
14 Gyration
15 Club
16 Plug
18 Equine
19 Ambush
21 Rufus
22 Abuzz
24 Junk

Solutions 251–252

251

Across:

1 Baron
4 Waist (Barren waste)
10 Palmist
11 Amble
12 Ditto
13 Attract
15 Ugly
17 Torso
19 Pithy
22 Aged
25 Article
27 Irate
29 Swoon
30 Intense
31 Realm
32 Scale

Down:

2 Allot
3 Ominous
5 Apart
6 Sabbath
7 Spade
8 Steal
9 Jetty
14 Type
16 Goal
18 Outcome
20 Idiotic
21 False
23 Genie
24 Jewel
26 Canal
28 Annul

252

Across:

1 Universe
5 City (University)
8 Elegance
9 Saga
11 Legislation
14 Moa
16 Rioja
17 Eon
18 Counterfeit
21 Brig
22 Advocate
24 Edge
25 Constant

Down:

1 Used
2 Ideal
3 Exaggerate
4 Sec
6 Imagine
7 Yearning
10 Cadaverous
12 Scour
13 Amicable
15 Amusing
19 Tiara
20 Rent
23 Duo

Solutions 253–254

253

Across:

1 Killer
5 Bight (Kilobyte)
9 Rearrange
10 Rig
11 Axe
12 Expedient
14 Hid
16 Teach
18 Tie
19 Attempted
21 Tin
22 Inn
23 Penniless
25 Grebe
26 Banter

Down:

2 Image
3 Largest
4 Run
5 Breed
6 Garment
7 Togetherness
8 Breathtaking
13 Plait
15 Detente
17 Hadrian
20 Maple
21 Theme
24 Nub

254

Across:

1 Purl
3 Fissures (Pearl-fishers)
9 Sugar
10 Bourbon
11 Orb
13 Hobgoblin
14 Pariah
16 Atrium
18 Identical
20 Nap
22 Trounce
23 Swamp
25 Seafarer
26 Deny

Down:

1 Pesto
2 Rug
4 Imbibe
5 Stub out
6 Rebellion
7 Synonym
8 Arch
12 Barcelona
14 Plinths
15 Antenna
17 Accede
19 Lose
21 Poppy
24 Ace

Solutions 255–256

255

Across:
1 Sank
3 Cherry (Sanctuary)
8 Compass
9 Rifle
10 Nudge
11 Open-air
12 Tavern
14 Cognac
17 Nightie
19 India
21 Nears
22 Tsunami
23 Attend
24 Dawn

Down:
1 Second-to-none
2 Nomad
3 Cosmos
4 Eerie
5 Refrain
6 Career
7 Depreciation
13 Vagrant
15 Odious
16 Heated
18 Taste
20 Drama

256

Across:
1 Havana
5 Bawl (Having a ball)
8 Shoe
9 Meditate
10 Probed
11 Tender
12 Incongruous
15 Strong
17 Stingy
19 Bulletin
20 Omit
21 Bend
22 Essays

Down:
2 Abhor
3 Acerbic
4 Armed
5 Baton
6 Witness
7 Editor
12 Intrude
13 Negate
14 Ominous
16 Ogled
17 Singe
18 Grimy

Solutions 257–258

257

Across:

1 Mount
4 Sate
7 Hung (Mao Tse-tung)
8 Aromatic
9 Illiberal
10 Age
12 Angler
14 Elated
16 Bet
18 Outskirts
21 Grandeur
22 Apex
23 Thug
24 Piece

Down:

1 Maudlin
2 Ungainly
3 Trade
4 Soak
5 Thing
6 Rotate
11 Salivate
13 Roused
15 Extreme
17 Earth
19 Strip
20 Snug

258

Across:

1 Canon
4 Pall (Cannonball)
7 Flog
8 Grenoble
9 Casserole
10 Bye
12 Heckle
14 Gauche
16 Apt
18 New Mexico
21 Tiramisu
22 Tool
23 Fete
24 Duchy

Down:

1 Collage
2 Nagasaki
3 Niger
4 Ploy
5 Lolly
6 Jet lag
11 Quixotic
13 Emetic
15 Hickory
17 Pride
19 Mould
20 Gaze

Solutions 259–260

259

Across:

1 Marques
5 Mann (Marksman)
7 Rowan
8 Bought
10 Epée
11 Tantrums
13 L-plate
14 Fiesta
17 Unafraid
19 Jump
21 Cavern
22 Craze
23 Eton
24 Pretext

Down:

1 Marvellous
2 Raw deal
3 Ulna
4 Subway
5 Mountain
6 Nehru
9 Escarpment
12 Sturgeon
15 Sausage
16 Kidnap
18 Adapt
20 Acre

260

Across:

1 Farther
5 Thyme (Father Time)
8 Zloty
9 Marimba
10 Discovery
12 Ism
13 Equity
14 Graphs
17 Job
18 Small arms
20 Yorkist
21 Xenon
23 Dodge
24 Endowed

Down:

1 Fazed
2 Rho
3 Hayloft
4 Rommel
5 Tarry
6 Yom Kippur
7 Erasmus
11 Slumbered
13 Enjoyed
15 Relaxed
16 Castle
18 Smile
19 Synod
22 Now

Solutions 261–262

261

Across:

1 Arts
5 Ends
7 Carafes (Arts and crafts)
8 Scorcher
10 Tort
12 Spot
14 Vicarage
16 Stressed
17 Cull
18 Plus
19 Downturn
22 Rostrum
23 Many
24 Brat

Down:

1 Amos
2 Scar
3 Archives
4 Afar
5 Esoteric
6 Salt
9 Capital
11 Regular
13 Treasury
15 Codeword
18 Prim
19 Dash
20 Tomb
21 Newt

262

Across:

1 Gnaw
3 Thumb
7 Rear (Northumbria)
8 Underwrite
9 Weak
12 Poltergeist
13 Nosey
15 Prang
19 Dreadnought
21 Shah
23 Impresario
24 Fawn
25 Odder
26 Bond

Down:

1 Grumpiness
2 Wrestle
3 Tawdry
4 Unisex
5 Brews
6 Gala
10 Etna
11 Knighthood
14 Soda
16 Rhubarb
17 Warped
18 Endear
20 Rhino
22 Hoax

Solutions 263–264

263

Across:		Down:	
1	Come	1	Croupier
3	Plea	2	Macaroni
9	Meant (Compliment)	4	Letter
10	Orchestra	5	Amateur
11	Talon	6	Pail
12	Persevere	7	Stun
15	Eunuch	8	Fete
17	Ormolu	13	Governor
19	Notoriety	14	Busybody
21	Mimic	16	Conceal
23	Esperanto	18	Steppe
24	Extra	20	Rare
25	Leer	21	Meet
26	Prey	22	Mute

264

Across:		Down:	
1	Shandy	1	Sapling
4	Leer (Chandelier)	2	Agree
8	Sparse	3	Deed
9	Exhume	5	Echelon
10	Rider	6	Remit
11	Athlete	7	Century
13	Agog	12	Assumed
15	Sir	14	Garbage
16	Near	17	Abandon
18	Amorous	19	Minus
20	Canal	21	Aisle
23	Inhale	22	Trio
24	Reside		
25	Seem		
26	Solemn		

Solutions 265–266

265

Across:
1 Sack
4 Sunny (Saxony)
8 Mongoose
9 Tact
10 Sour
11 Hilarity
12 Mellow
14 Bolero
16 Parmesan
19 Just
20 Lima
21 Lukewarm
22 Start
23 Kelp

Down:
2 Anger
3 Know-how
4 Steal
5 Natural
6 Yacht
7 Morose
13 Lambada
14 Bangkok
15 Resort
17 Aries
18 Split
19 Jewel

266

Across:
1 Lack
4 Err
6 Daze
8 Sickle (Lackadaisical)
9 Guffaw
10 Decrepit
11 Riot
12 Dog's breakfast
17 Used
19 Assembly
22 Muesli
23 Ailing
24 Bevy
25 Eve
26 Dart

Down:
2 Alike
3 Kakuros
4 Eye up
5 Regatta
6 Defer
7 Zealous
10 Dud
13 Obscure
14 Realise
15 Fumbled
16 Tay
18 Dishy
20 Shave
21 Loner

Solutions 267–268

267

Across:
1 Note
3 Hawking (No talking)
8 Adjoin
9 Radish
10 Mediates
11 Shed
12 Shield
15 Legate
17 Bull
19 Presence
22 Stalls
23 Ransom
24 Educate
25 Odes

Down:
1 Nudge
2 Two-time
4 Aerosol
5 Kudos
6 Nascent
7 Gnat
13 Haunted
14 Deposit
16 Gleaned
18 Lilac
20 Earl
21 Crops

268

Across:
1 Annoy
4 Foreign
8 Aye (An eye for an eye)
9 Nor
10 Venus
11 Maybe
12 Utensil
15 Espy
17 Digest
19 Psyche
22 Alec
24 Salvage
26 Rogue
28 Shrug
30 Ate
31 Own
32 Immerse
33 Hotel

Down:
1 Alarmed
2 Needy
3 Yankees
4 Fire up
5 Revue
6 Inn
7 Nasal
13 Type
14 Sic
16 Stag
18 Gel
20 Screech
21 Eternal
23 Legate
24 Sushi
25 Anger
27 Gloat
29 Ram

Solutions 269–270

269

Across:
1 Pin
3 Err
5 Four (Pinafore)
7 Rogue
8 Colour
10 Suet
11 Schmaltz
13 Patrol
14 Unique
17 Montreal
19 Fiji
21 Voyage
22 Rebut
23 Weld
24 Nub
25 Eon

Down:
1 Parish-pump
2 Neglect
3 Even
4 Rococo
5 Filament
6 Usual
9 Uzbekistan
12 Gourmand
15 Quibble
16 Careen
18 Noose
20 Grub

270

Across:
1 Mess
4 Hush
8 Meet (Messerschmitt)
9 Available
11 Energy
13 Setting
15 Scurry
16 Tactic
18 Sketch
20 Debris
22 Holiday
23 Review
25 Alleviate
26 Mesh
27 Fret
28 Hope

Down:
2 Envy
3 Shiver
4 Hearty
5 Silent
6 Territory
7 Stay
10 Engaged
12 Asks
13 Supervise
14 Trachea
17 Cost
19 Howler
20 Direct
21 Banish
23 Rump
24 Step

Solutions 271–272

271

Across:		Down:	
1	Myrrh	2	Yarns
4	Cater (Mercator)	3	Request
10	Baroque	5	Asses
11	Sheer	6	Electra
12	Ensue	7	Abbey
13	Lesotho	8	Jelly
15	Soya	9	Arrow
17	Plato	14	Ears
19	Rajah	16	Ooze
22	Zest	18	Lifting
25	Waffled	20	At large
27	Lithe	21	Sweep
29	Exile	23	Edict
30	Carvery	24	Pepys
31	Egret	26	Liege
32	Gecko	28	Tweak

272

Across:		Down:	
1	Braking	1	Bamboozled
5	Gnus (Breaking news)	2	Antwerp
7	Mitre	3	Item
8	Amoeba	4	Gravel
10	Oxen	5	Geometry
11	Demeaned	6	Urban
13	Zephyr	9	Adjustment
14	Ormolu	12	Hydrogen
17	Entirely	15	Opulent
19	Quit	16	Flinch
21	Margin	18	Teach
22	Theme	20	Stab
23	Shun		
24	Habitat		

Solutions 273–274

273

Across:
1 Salve
4 Adored
8 Ali (Salvador Dali)
9 Horseshoe
10 Truncheon
12 Roo
13 Roe
14 Balsa
15 Tat
16 Rib
18 Gatehouse
20 Ivy League
22 Awe
23 Surrey
24 A-list

Down:
1 Scatterbrain
2 Leisure
3 Ethic
4 Air
5 Oceania
6 Ether
7 Below the belt
11 Eilat
14 Bugbear
15 Tsunami
17 Bayou
19 Hyena
21 Guy

274

Across:
1 Suss
4 Pens
8 Full (Suspenseful)
9 Joan of Arc
11 Vortex
13 Citizen
15 Proton
16 Dictum
18 Tomcat
20 Begone
22 Cameron
23 Medici
25 Ownership
26 Kith
27 Knit
28 Pike

Down:
2 Upon
3 Sunlit
4 Puffin
5 Nerved
6 Quotation
7 Flex
10 Conifer
12 Spot
13 Commodity
14 Tobacco
17 Meek
19 Taiwan
20 Bereft
21 Gossip
23 Make
24 Pink

Solutions 275–276

275

Across:		Down:	
1	Knight	1	Kennel
4	Mayor (Nightmare)	2	Inexact
8	Needy	3	Haystack
9	Rampant	4	Mime
10	Enacted	5	Yearn
11	Gnat	6	Rotate
12	Era	7	Crude
14	Otic	13	Amenable
15	Mock	16	Courage
18	Keg	17	Candid
21	Afar	19	Globe
23	Languid	20	Adhere
25	Disturb	22	Aisle
26	Blame	24	Fuss
27	Dress		
28	Delete		

276

Across:		Down:	
1	Forger	1	Falcon
4	Check (Forge a cheque)	2	Regatta
8	Light	3	Entirely
9	Abandon	4	Coax
10	Ontario	5	Elder
11	Free	6	Kennel
12	Cub	7	Havoc
14	Fall	13	Brethren
15	Roam	16	Avocado
18	Yam	17	Absent
21	Ball	19	Moose
23	Outcome	20	Vermin
25	Endless	22	Ladle
26	Realm	24	Feat
27	Theft		
28	Enjoin		

Solutions 277–278

277

Across:
1 Wrick
4 Shore (Rickshaw)
8 Octopus
9 Ample
10 Gratification
11 Design
12 Studio
15 Ungrammatical
18 Liner
19 Tantrum
20 Enemy
21 Arson

Down:
1 Wrong
2 Intransigence
3 Kipling
4 Siskin
5 Osaka
6 Esprit de corps
7 Lean-to
11 Double
13 Titania
14 Smithy
16 Agree
17 Lemon

278

Across:
1 Roared
5 Eels (Raw deals)
8 Seem
9 Millrace
10 Patron
11 Virtue
12 Pleasurable
15 Angler
17 Fiasco
19 Viscount
20 Arid
21 Lead
22 Hooker

Down:
2 Opera
3 Remorse
4 Demon
5 Error
6 Lecture
7 Clever
12 Pensive
13 Sprout
14 Bravado
16 Lucid
17 Fetch
18 Crime

Solutions 279–280

279

Across:

1 Duel
3 Bees
9 Hoary (You'll be sorry)
10 Accompany
11 Noted
12 Reminisce
15 Breech
17 Asleep
19 Lethargic
21 Entry
23 Potassium
24 Risks
25 Oust
26 Mean

Down:

1 Diatribe
2 Encumber
4 Elapse
5 Shyness
6 Vast
7 Dyed
8 Omen
13 Re-ignite
14 Specimen
16 Calypso
18 Status
20 Apse
21 Earn
22 Task

280

Across:

1 Undies
4 Hirer
8 Bulls (Undesirables)
9 Lengthy
10 Nigeria
11 Loch
12 Elk
14 Stun
15 Iris
18 God
21 Oust
23 In-depth
25 Gondola
26 Evoke
27 Dress
28 Aspect

Down:

1 Urbane
2 Delight
3 Ensuring
4 Hind
5 Ratio
6 Rhythm
7 Algae
13 Kindness
16 Improve
17 Dogged
19 Divan
20 Threat
22 Sense
24 Hogs

Solutions 281–282

281

Across:
- **1** Coat
- **3** Dour
- **6** Own (Côtes du Rhône)
- **9** Awkward
- **10** Idiom
- **11** Radio
- **12** Awesome
- **13** Scanty
- **15** Crisis
- **18** Overdue
- **20** Minus
- **23** Blaze
- **24** Servile
- **25** Rue
- **26** Mist
- **27** Bent

Down:
- **1** Chair
- **2** Asked
- **4** Ordeal
- **5** Raise
- **6** Ominous
- **7** Numbers
- **8** Cavort
- **13** Slobber
- **14** Average
- **16** Remark
- **17** Versus
- **19** Dream
- **21** Naive
- **22** Scent

282

Across:
- **1** Moaner
- **4** Leaser (Mona Lisa)
- **9** Dates
- **10** Reading
- **11** Era
- **12** Small
- **13** Noisier
- **15** Atmospheric
- **19** Muddier
- **20** Awake
- **21** Egg
- **22** Session
- **24** Exits
- **25** Doting
- **26** Stands

Down:
- **1** Modest
- **2** Attracted
- **3** Easel
- **5** Examine
- **6** Ski
- **7** Regard
- **8** Transparent
- **14** Imitation
- **16** Opinion
- **17** Amused
- **18** Tenses
- **20** Agent
- **23** Set

Solutions 283–284

283

Across:
1 Tacks
4 Pair (Taxpayer)
8 Primula
9 Adage
10 Rider
11 Anodyne
13 Caruso
15 Thrace
17 Abdomen
20 Bleat
22 Edgar
23 Extorts
24 Flay
25 Thyme

Down:
1 Tapir
2 Child prodigy
3 Squares
4 Plaza
5 Idaho
6 Lady Jane Grey
7 Revere
12 Nut
13 Coaxed
14 Owe
16 Habitat
18 Moral
19 Needy
21 Taste

284

Across:
1 Flow
3 Tiller (Flotilla)
9 Matlock
10 Tacit
11 Rag
12 Quadrille
13 Bandit
14 Height
16 Impatient
19 Zip
21 Cupid
22 Proctor
23 Export
24 Levy

Down:
1 Femur
2 Octagon
4 Interjection
5 Local
6 Retreat
7 Conquistador
8 Skua
13 Brioche
15 Gazette
17 Pop-up
18 Espy
20 Party

The Telegraph

Solutions 285–286

285

Across:		Down:	
1	Hyde	2	Yawn
4	Dell	3	Earwax
8	Vice (Edelweiss)	4	Design
9	Swordsman	5	Leader
11	Doctor	6	Jitterbug
13	Wangled	7	Fear
15	Klaxon	10	No doubt
16	Roared	12	Skim
18	Metric	13	Wast Water
20	Abrupt	14	Nominal
22	Name tag	17	Data
23	Quasar	19	Career
25	Leviathan	20	Aerial
26	Ibex	21	Raptor
27	Oral	23	Quit
28	Rhyl	24	Zany

286

Across:		Down:	
1	Suffolk	1	Snuff
5	Eight (Suffocate)	2	Few
8	Unwed	3	Oddball
9	Boudoir	4	Kybosh
10	Fricassee	5	Exude
12	Tan	6	Ghost town
13	Puddle	7	Tyranny
14	Spooky	11	Indonesia
17	Tun	13	Pitfall
18	Memoranda	15	Parasol
20	Arsenal	16	Emblem
21	Sabre	18	Manna
23	Llama	19	Akela
24	Malaria	22	Bar

Solutions 287–288

287

Across:
1 Kernel
4 Bogie (Colonel Bogey)
8 Rupee
9 Adamant
10 Tsunami
11 Star
12 Den
14 Zero
15 Oval
18 Rue
21 Ruin
23 Visitor
25 Altered
26 Niece
27 Early
28 Jersey

Down:
1 Karate
2 Rapture
3 Elevator
4 Bias
5 Grant
6 Entire
7 Rapid
13 Nonsense
16 Artless
17 Create
19 Evade
20 Artery
22 Inter
24 Prey

288

Across:
1 Whine
4 Liszt (Wine list)
10 Advance
11 State
12 Tulip
13 Awesome
15 Idle
17 Prune
19 Prise
22 Alto
25 Austere
27 Bacon
29 Early
30 Precede
31 Jetty
32 Sylph

Down:
2 Hovel
3 Ninepin
5 Issue
6 Zealous
7 Earth
8 Legal
9 Jewel
14 Wept
16 Dear
18 Reserve
20 Robbery
21 Camel
23 Leapt
24 Anger
26 Egypt
28 Cheap

Solutions 289–290

289

Across:
1 Whorls
5 Treat (Wall Street)
9 Postponed
10 Ego
11 Eye
12 Esperanto
14 Doe
16 Exact
18 Leg
19 Artichoke
21 Sob
22 Lie
23 Nightmare
25 Dwell
26 Greedy

Down:
2 Haste
3 Replete
4 Sin
5 Tudor
6 Eternal
7 Thoroughbred
8 Spread-eagled
13 Piano
15 Extreme
17 Theatre
20 Canal
21 Stand
24 Gig

290

Across:
4 Canter
5 Loop (Cantaloupe)
7 Breadth
10 Avert
11 Deserve
12 Onion
14 Conduct
15 Midas
16 Vivaldi
20 Tacit
21 Neonate
22 Dare
23 Supply

Down:
1 Knead
2 Keats
3 Convent
4 Cork
6 Pardon
8 Deposit
9 Headman
10 Avocado
13 Wizard
14 Caviare
17 Lemur
18 Inept
19 Stay

Solutions 291–292

291

Across:		Down:	
1	Why	1	Whip
3	Sold	2	Yarn
5	Howl (Wise old owl)	3	Settlement
8	Irritate	4	Latvia
10	Stun	6	Outburst
11	Pin	7	Lingered
13	Route	9	Ringo
14	Aggregate	12	Precocious
16	Don	14	Adjacent
17	See	15	Gnashing
19	Exploited	18	Eerie
21	Arson	20	Primer
22	Sit	22	Stem
24	Edit	23	Trap
25	Imposter		
26	Toga		
27	Errs		
28	Map		

292

Across:		Down:	
1	Sacks	1	Summit
4	Oaf	2	Cask
6	Own (Saxophone)	3	Sneak
8	Miscellaneous	4	Oil
9	Kneel	5	Finally
11	Tins	6	Odometer
13	Lithe	7	Nestle
14	Tardy	10	Eyrie
15	Mouth	12	Neurosis
16	Prow	14	Thimble
18	Inert	15	Marina
21	Insubordinate	17	Wheeze
23	Ass	19	Tripe
24	Eye	20	Caps
25	Ensue	22	Rue

Solutions 293–294

293

Across:

1	Inn
3	Speck
6	Tor
8	Lewes (Inspector Lewis)
9	Ranking
10	Snowmobile
12	Ear
15	Ogle
17	Tell
18	Den
22	Kick around
25	Crumpet
26	Tutsi
27	Tat
28	Rural
29	Lag

Down:

1	Illusion
2	New World
3	Sesame
4	Enrobe
5	Kindle
6	Trio
7	Rage
11	Eat
13	Rebuttal
14	Cladding
16	Eek
19	Nipper
20	Skater
21	Brutal
23	Scat
24	Cult

294

Across:

1	Car
3	Bide
5	Rate (Carbohydrate)
8	Absolute
10	Pail
11	Tot
13	Sumps
14	Detergent
16	Ado
17	See
19	Alienated
21	Books
22	Sit
24	Edge
25	Jawbones
26	Kind
27	Fete
28	Bar

Down:

1	Chat
2	Rest
3	Balderdash
4	Dotage
6	Alarmist
7	Enlisted
9	Bored
12	Ostensible
14	Daybreak
15	Toboggan
18	Eerie
20	Insane
22	Snub
23	Tsar

Solutions 295–296

295

Across:
1 Hearse
4 Hoot (Hirsute)
8 Allure
9 Asleep
10 Offer
11 Bouquet
13 Oxen
15 Arc
16 Yale
18 Warm-ups
20 Spade
23 Gerbil
24 Trivia
25 Teak
26 Swathe

Down:
1 Halifax
2 Acute
3 Suez
5 Obloquy
6 Theme
7 Majorca
12 Walpole
14 Namibia
17 Luddite
19 Agent
21 Print
22 Stow

296

Across:
1 Mourning
7 Starr (Morning star)
8 Otherwise
9 Ass
10 Hope
11 Cellar
13 Voyage
14 Adjust
17 Falcon
18 Soap
20 Due
22 Tactician
23 Crazy
24 External

Down:
1 Mooch
2 Unhappy
3 Norm
4 Nailed
5 Qatar
6 Brisket
7 Seclude
12 Agility
13 Viaduct
15 Utopian
16 Coccyx
17 Feral
19 Panel
21 Five

Solutions 297–298

297

Across:
1 Venice
4 Whaler (Venezuela)
7 Gangling
9 Oedipus
12 Therm
13 Boris
15 Rabbi
16 Annie
17 Arden
18 Demon
19 Nostrum
23 Regional
24 Brazil
25 Chilly

Down:
1 Vegetarian
2 Non-members
3 Columbia
4 Wage
5 Asti
6 Esau
8 Notre-Dame
10 Phenomenal
11 Screenplay
14 Sandwich
20 Over
21 Tizz
22 Ural

298

Across:
1 Antic
4 Lime
8 Axe (Anticlimax)
9 Cafeteria
10 Myth
11 Lucretia
12 Cap
13 Catchy
14 Yum-yum
16 Les
17 Step on it
18 Grin
20 Hitch-hike
21 Two
22 Yo-yo
23 Kayak

Down:
1 Anaemic
2 Twenty-twenty
3 Coco
4 Lift up
5 Motor bus
6 Pretty-pretty
7 Ha-ha
11 Lay
12 Choo-choo
14 Yet
15 Menfolk
16 Libido
17 Soho
19 Beck

Solutions 299–300

299

Across:

1	Polly
3	Titian (Politician)
7	Roquefort
9	Meet
10	Nigh
11	Anger
13	Trophy
14	Eyrie
15	Clear
17	Dealer
20	Deter
21	Mace
23	Atom
24	Talkative
25	Stolen
26	Urban

Down:

1	Permit
2	Loot
3	Toffee
4	Torn
5	Night
6	Funny
7	Recollect
8	Titillate
11	Ahead
12	Ryder
16	Reckon
17	Death
18	Remain
19	Amass
22	Earl
23	Aver

300

Across:

1	Counter
5	Feat (Counterfeit)
7	Plain
8	Chintz
10	Tear
11	Lethargy
13	Leered
14	August
17	Tattered
19	Scar
21	Career
22	Credo
23	Lazy
24	Humerus

Down:

1	Capitulate
2	Unaware
3	Tiny
4	Racket
5	Faithful
6	Alter
9	Mysterious
12	Cemetery
15	Unclear
16	Search
18	Tiara
20	Scam

Solutions 301–302

301

Across:

1 Purr
5 Know (Pernod)
7 Obtrude
8 Gershwin
10 Pomp
12 Stud
14 Wiseacre
16 Catalyst
17 Etui
18 Myth
19 Specimen
22 Anodyne
23 Feud
24 Apse

Down:

1 Plug
2 Ross
3 Stowaway
4 Ruin
5 Keepsake
6 Whip
9 Estuary
11 Marquee
13 Dead-head
15 Sotheby's
18 Miff
19 Slow
20 Idea
21 Nave

302

Across:

1 Reef
4 Reign (Refrain)
8 Anorexia
9 Moby
10 Pour
11 Reminder
12 Permit
14 Sleuth
16 Friendly
19 Stew
20 Dick
21 Maturity
22 Enter
23 Rite

Down:

2 Error
3 Foxtrot
4 Realm
5 Immense
6 Noble
7 Income
13 Meerkat
14 Shyster
15 Treaty
17 Raise
18 Demur
19 Strut

Solutions 303

303

Across:

1 Flea
3 Tear
6 Arm (Fleet Air Arm)
9 Once and for all
10 Bank card
12 Thai
13 Ear
15 Laptop
18 Buddha
19 New
21 Peel
22 Graffiti
25 Orchestration
26 Sad
27 Rare
28 Oral

Down:

1 Football pools
2 Ex-con
4 Endure
5 Rook
6 Abashed
7 Multinational
8 Halcyon
11 Dab
14 Ruffian
16 Pierced
17 Peg
20 Writer
23 Icier
24 Bear